Counselling the Elderly and

D0267147

WT £45 TER
230

BASIC TEXTS IN COUNSELLING AND PSYCHOTHERAPY

Series Editor: Stephen Frosh

This series introduces readers to the theory and practice of counselling and psychotherapy across a wide range of topic areas. The books will appeal to anyone wishing to use counselling and psychotherapeutic skills and will be particularly relevant to workers in health, education, social work and related settings.

The books in this series are unusual in being rooted in psychodynamic and systemic ideas, yet being written at an accessible, readable and introductory level. Each text offers theoretical background and guidance for practice, with creative use of clinical examples.

Published

Jenny Altschuler
WORKING WITH CHRONIC ILLNESS

Paul Terry
COUNSELLING THE ELDERLY AND THEIR CARERS

Forthcoming

Sheila Ernst, Bill Barnes and Keith Hyde
AN INTRODUCTION TO GROUPWORK

Gill Gorell Barnes
COUNSELLING FAMILIES

Jan Wiener and Mannie Sher
COUNSELLING AND PSYCHOTHERAPY IN PRIMARY HEALTH CARE

Series Standing Order

If you would like to receive future titles in this series as they are published, you can make use of our standing order facility. To place a standing order please contact your bookseller or, in case of difficulty, write to us at the address below with your name and address and the name of the series. Please state with which title you wish to begin your standing order. (If you live outside the UK we may not have the rights for your area, in which case we will forward your order to the publisher concerned.)

Standing Order Service, Macmillan Distribution Ltd,
Houndmills, Basingstoke, Hampshire, RG21 6XS, England

COUNSELLING THE ELDERLY AND THEIR CARERS

PAUL TERRY

MACMILLAN

First published 1997 by
MACMILLAN PRESS LTD
Houndmills, Basingstoke, Hampshire RG21 6XS
and London
Companies and representatives
throughout the world

ISBN 0–333–62011–9

A catalogue record for this book is available
from the British Library.

This book is printed on paper suitable for recycling and
made from fully managed and sustained forest sources.

10 9 8 7 6 5 4 3 2 1
06 05 04 03 02 01 00 99 98 97

Printed in Hong Kong

For my parents, Win and Ted Terry
and our friend Sadie Joseph

CONTENTS

PART II: WORKING WITH CARE STAFF AND THE ELDERLY

FOREWORD

Counselling the elderly is the sort of work that probably most of us wouldn't want to do and may not even particularly want to read about, much less think that we can learn from to help us in other areas of counselling and institutional life. This book goes some way towards shattering all those reservations: it is engrossing to read, it does have much to teach us about counselling and institutional life far from the world of the aged and dying, and it is heartening in conveying that this work can be deeply appreciated by the recipients, patients and workers alike, and is maturing for those who undertake it.

In the opening chapter of the book the author states that this book is about an approach to work with the elderly. It is the psychodynamic approach, drawing on the deep insights provided by psychoanalysis into the inner world of patients and on the resources of the therapeutic relationship to illuminate that inner world. The first half of the book is about this, about work with elderly individuals and couples. Paul Terry writes without sentiment or heroics about mind-jangling internal and external chaos, about 'loneliness without remedy', and about grieving for the loss of the ability to live the life that is left in a body deserted by the faculties that seem essential for living. He writes about a variety of situations, ranging from work with couples who in the context of this book are facing the quite ordinary ambiguity of which partner will die first, through many different examples of personal and family responses to dying, to an extended *in extremis* piece of work with a man without speech, requiring the ultimate in the therapeutic stance of not knowing so that the unknown can emerge almost exclusively through the counter-transference and through sensitivity to the smallest of signs in the grossest of conditions. Just at the point where there seems nothing left to say or little point in saying it as death draws the patient away, it's evident that being given a hearing and a response allows these patients an almost unimaginable opportunity to settle their internal relationships before they go.

The essential quality of this work is the capacity never to forget that these people are facing death, confronting the fact that there is no way around this, but also never to forget that no matter how damaged, debilitated or almost dead they are as a result of their age and illness, they are still alive and their inner world is still there to be worked with.

The second half of the book goes beyond the usual clinical boundary to explore the effect of the institutional environment on the patients and those who work with them: the staff, the key-workers and the managers. The climax of the book describes the author's innovative attempt to hold a weekly ward group with patients and staff where their relationship to each other and to their shared institution is the focus of attention. This group is sheer mayhem much of the time but even so it resolves into a final minor chord of most moving and *understandable* sadness.

This whole section of the book builds particularly on the classical study by Menzies on social structures as a defence against anxiety and demonstrates without doubt the importance of this approach in maintaining the sanity of the staff and protecting the staff and patients from the enactments of mutual sadism provoked by the frustrations and disappointments of their shared circumstances. It happens that the period of work described in the book coincides with the transition of long-stay care units to privatised management, so another layer of loss and change is added to the work.

The refreshing and enlivening quality of this book rests on its utter simplicity. It is an account of a very experienced counsellor using his experiences as a beginner in this field of work to revisit some fundamental psychodynamic concepts and psychotherapeutic techniques. His use of theory is very restrained and parsimonious. There are perhaps a half-dozen theoretical points in the book: the centrality of unconscious projective mechanisms in personal and professional relationships in individual, group and institutional settings; the cause and effects of social defences in the life of an institution; the importance of understanding the meaning of indi-vidual acts as indicators of institutional dynamics; the secondary effects of disability; the origins and management of abuse in work-ing relationships; the responses to loss and change; and the indis-pensability of the transference and counter-transference in understanding the primitive anxieties of these patients and staff.

This minimalist but amply sufficient framework puts the burden of the narrative on the casework described in the book. The extended case material is not overworked so that the readers can develop their own ideas about patients and the working relation-ships. (Furthermore it avoids the confused and potentially diverting debate over what is physical and what is psychological in the patients' condition by focusing steadfastly on what is presented within the relationships with the counsellor, workers, and other patients.) This combination of trim theory and rich case material leaves the reader with memorable messages. It is easy to remember, for instance, that only when staff can undo their identification with their patients and restore themselves to their own role as key-workers or managers can they be of any use to themselves or their patients. Doing it is harder, and this book is evidence of the skill the author brings to the work both in keeping himself in role as counsellor and in working consultatively with the staff in their roles while also obviously having to face his own mortality and anxieties about the future of the service.

'My mother died a long time ago and now she is living in a nursing home. I haven't seen her in years.' The person who made this remark meant that her mother-as-she-knew-her 'died' as a result of a stroke. This book is about how 'my-mother-as-she-knew-herself' has to live with her diminished self in perpetual mourning and how carers see her day by day. It is a completely different kind of *memento mori*, and indeed almost every patient in the book is now dead, but this is their fine and generous legacy. It is written in a clear and steady voice with truly depressive optimism. If that sounds like a contradiction in terms, then read on and let the book explain itself.

ELLEN NOONAN

Head of Counselling Section
Centre for Extra-Mural Studies
Birkbeck College
University of London

Acknowledgements

I would like to express my gratitude to the elderly patients and their carers who have taught me about the experience of being elderly and being a carer. For reasons of confidentiality I cannot name individuals or the hospital in which the work took place. I would especially like to thank the hospital manager, her deputy and the clinical psychology manager for their unfailing support and encouragement; and my supervisor, Maggie Cohen, and my analyst for enabling me to sustain and develop the work.

I had the benefit of consultation about the organisational aspects of the work from David Armstrong, then Director of the Grubb Insitute, now at the Tavistock Clinic; and from Eric Miller at the Tavistock Institute of Human Relations.

In the preparation of this book my editor, Stephen Frosh, gave me his careful and thoughtful attention to the drafts in comments which helped me develop the writing about the work. My colleague, Ellen Noonan, also gave generously in her usual perspicacious comments and then preparing the foreword. Thanks also to Keith Povey for the copy-editing and supervision of the production of this book.

My thanks to Graham Thompson for joining me in some of this work and for agreeing to the inclusion of some material from our work.

I would like to thank my students and colleagues in the Counselling Section of the Centre for Extra-Mural Studies at Birkbeck College from whom I have learned so much about counselling, its application to different settings, working with the organisation and writing about the work.

The author and publishers are grateful to Dr A. H. Mann for giving permission to quote the words of the song *Danny Boy*.

Finally, my love and gratitude to those who have suffered the labour and birth pangs of this book.

PAUL TERRY

INTRODUCTION

Does my way of seeing it help you to see it more clearly your way? (Waddell, 1991)

I find this question immensely inspiring as a goal for counselling, and for this book about counselling. Margot Waddell asked the question when describing the importance of *following* the client, which she illustrated by a beautiful image of 'holding a candle behind the individual, the better to illuminate what lies before, rather than shining a directive pedagogic light in front, to lead'. In this book, I shall be writing about my experience of working with elderly people and their carers by describing their words and actions, and my thoughts and feelings when with them, based on notes I kept about the work. I have included my reflections as I sifted through these experiences in supervision, personal analysis and in discussions with colleagues who helped me as I prepared this manuscript. My hope is that my way of seeing these experiences will help you, the reader, see your experiences with the elderly, or perhaps of being elderly, more clearly your way.

The book is the story of my introduction to working with the elderly after I took up a new post for a clinical psychologist in a geriatric service for 'the elderly physically frail'. I was based in a long-stay hospital, also called 'continuing care'. Various changes had been made in the service: a keyworking system was established whereby patients were assigned to named carers, staff were taken out of uniforms and the hospital environment was made more homely. My brief from the management was to support and encourage beneficial change in the service.

I have written about the first three years until the management of the long-stay service was transferred from the National Health Service (NHS) to a private company. At the same time the patients and staff were re-housed in two newly constructed, purpose-built nursing homes. During these three years the work concentrated on staff and patients in the long-stay hospital, but it also included some counselling of patients and their families who were on a rehabilitation ward and some elderly people who were referred as out-patients, by their general practitioners (GPs) or the consultant physicians. In the context of this work 'elderly' means over sixty-five, following the traditional definition as post-retirement, and the age from which patients could be admitted into long-stay care. Because I was based in a hospital I refer to this client group as 'patients'.

The elderly people I write about in this book include a few of the 'young-old' meaning those who are 'still active physically and mentally, may hope to enjoy not having to work for a living and having time for other activities'. Most of the work reported is with the 'old-old', those for whom 'bodily and mental frailty becomes more evident and physical disabilities are inevitable' (Neugarten quoted by Porter, 1991). I don't like these labels, but they are useful because they draw attention to two different stages of life for the elderly. I shall also be writing about a third stage in which elderly people can experience a dreadful transition from an active hopeful state into a physically debilitated one. But I shall try to avoid labels because they can be misused as a way of distancing ourselves from the experience of being old.

This book is as much about *an approach* to the work as it is about the nature of the specific experiences of elderly patients and their carers. The approach draws on psychodynamic counselling and is based on the application of psycho-analytic ideas to counselling in varied work settings, in order to understand unconscious processes in individuals, groups, institutions and society. Thus, in parallel with individual counselling, this approach included working with the institution of the long-stay hospital. It meant thinking about the effect of the institution on the counselling work and promoting change within the institution by working with care staff and management. Underlying this perspective is the understanding, derived from psycho-analytical studies, that individuals may express difficulties on behalf of others with whom they live and work and that institutions like hospitals can develop systems of working which militate against the best interests of patients and staff. Further, however much change may be desired it can also bring conscious and unconscious opposition, because of the ripples or waves it may produce. For example, it is usually recognised that therapeutic work with children needs to be supported by parallel work with their parents. The elderly are in a comparable position because they are often highly dependent on their carers and may therefore meet powerful opposition if they attempt to change.

Likewise care staff are in a dependent position in relation to management, and change in carers needs to be supported by work with management.

I have written about the work as a case study of my experiences because of the interest in understanding and working with the institutional setting and to keep in mind the particular context in which the counselling took place. In the time covered by this book, the hospital was going through changes which mirrored some of the ageing processes in its elderly patients. The very fabric of the hospital building was deteriorating beyond repair as plans were made to move to new nursing homes and the NHS purchasers awarded the management of the services to a private company. I was witnessing the demise of the hospital and the NHS management of the service. Hence it was crucial to understand how the institutional processes might be affecting staff and patients because what was happening in the institution so closely resembled issues of change and loss facing the patients.

When I planned to write this book as a case study, my editor, Stephen Frosh, was concerned it could be too particular for a general introduction to this work. I have tried to address this concern by drawing attention to general principles in the work. Each section of the chapters has a boxed introduction to alert the reader to some of the themes in the work which I believe are applicable for others working with the elderly in different roles and settings. Elsewhere key concepts and their definitions are in *italic*.

I have divided the book into two parts. Part I is an account of counselling work with elderly patients, sometimes with their spouses and families. *Chapter 1* begins with a description of my understanding of psychodynamic counselling by explaining some of the psycho-analytic ideas on which it is based, its aim and the particular contribution of psycho-analytic work with the elderly. *Chapter 2* is an account of some of my early work in response to the referrals: offering brief counselling to patients, mainly to those who were admitted to the rehabilitation ward following an acute illness, essentially working with patients' and carers' grief. *Chapter 3* is about some longer work, counselling elderly out-patients, where some of the deeper issues which unfolded were about the emotional reactions to ageing and the anticipation of death. *Chapter 4* describes some counselling of elderly couples and particular issues about sustaining relationships and at the same time facing one's own death or being left alone and losing a lifelong relationship. *Chapter 5* concludes Part I with a case study of my work with an elderly man who, following a stroke, had lost his capacity to talk, work which led me to some of the unspeakable experiences of being old and of being a carer.

Part II of the book describes my work with staff and patients in the long-stay hospital. *Chapter 6* introduces some of the theoretical contributions of psycho-analysis to understanding institutions and to working with people with multiple handicap. *Chapter 7* describes the institutional setting seen through the eyes of a young clinical psychology trainee, whom I supervised as he grappled with the emotional experience of elderly patients living on the ward. *Chapter 8* is an account of some individual work with staff who were keyworkers, the named carers of patients on the long-stay wards, which gave some insight into the care giving relationship: its satisfactions and frustrations, and how it might lead to abusive practices. *Chapter 9* is about working with staff support groups in the hospital during a period of turbulence and change, trying to help staff continue to hold their patients in mind in increasingly uncertain and unstable circumstances. *Chapter 10* describes some of the issues facing the managers of the hospital service in this period of change and transfer to the private sector. *Chapter 11* is an account of innovating meetings for patients and staff from the long-stay wards which were aimed at addressing deadly institutionalisation and lack of contact on these wards.

The book ends with *Conclusions* about the work derived from my own emotional experience of being with the elderly and their carers; and with an *Epilogue* which gives a short account of work in progress following the change of management and the move to the new nursing homes.

In the book names of staff and patients have been changed to preserve anonymity. I have used the masculine pronoun for reasons of stylistic simplicity.

Lastly, I feel I should add the equivalent of the government health warning because the material in the book is extremely painful. Being based in long-stay care meant that much of my contact has been with those who are very old and very ill, continuing to live despite terrible debilitating illnesses. The elderly who struggle to survive under these conditions and those who care for them need huge resources of patience, good will and courage. I feel privileged to have joined these elderly people and their carers and I hope I have conveyed something of the enjoyment that comes from the engagement with them.

THE ELDERLY AND THEIR RELATIVES

THE THEORETICAL UNDERPINNING OF THE COUNSELLING WORK

Introduction

This chapter is intended to provide an overview of psycho-analytic theory which I find useful for the work reported in the rest of the book. It is therefore selective and by no means a comprehensive account of the different schools of psycho-analytic thought. The chapter can only be an introduction to some quite complex concepts. (For the reader who is interested in a more general introduction see Symington, 1986, and Bateman and Holmes, 1995; or for a more detailed exposition of the particular concepts in this chapter see Segal, 1973, and Salzberger-Wittenberg, 1970).

The chapter begins with some of the early discoveries in psycho-analysis made by Sigmund Freud and Melanie Klein. There follows a detailed account of Klein's description of the emotional experience of the infant, particularly unconscious phantasies, which underlie anxieties and defences and developing states of mind present from birth. It may seem odd to spend so much space on an account of infantile development in a book about the elderly. The reason is that Klein and her followers have shown that these infantile anxieties return throughout the life cycle, provoked by various kinds of stress, especially loss and grief. I find these ideas helpful in working with the elderly who often experience painful loss toward the end of their lives, facing the ultimate loss of life itself. However, for the elderly there is additional pain in the revival of these infantile feelings because, unlike the infant for whom the anxieties accompany development and growth, in the elderly they accompany physical and mental decline with ensuing helplessness and dependency.

Basic concepts for psychodynamic counselling

The unconscious, transference and counter-transference

One very hot summer evening in 1883, when Freud was just 27 and completing his medical studies, he heard about some remarkable events which were to lead him to even more remarkable discoveries. He had joined a senior medical colleague, his old friend and mentor, Joseph Breuer, for a late supper. Freud and Breuer discussed the treatment of Breuer's patient, 'Anna O'. Breuer had taken an exceptional interest in this young woman. He listened attentively to her thoughts about the psychological disturbances she suffered and together they evolved what she called her 'talking cure'. They found that under states of hypnosis she could recall various 'unconscious' memories which were associated with her disturbing symptoms and when she did so the symptoms disappeared. Apparently the treatment had been successfully completed the year before, but on this summer evening Breuer revealed to Freud that when he went to pay a final visit to Anna O he found her going through an imagined childbirth, believing she was delivering Breuer's child. Breuer was so shocked by this experience he never pursued psychotherapeutic work again.

I think Freud learned a great deal from this story, not least the value of listening to and following patients in their discoveries. He came to understand how unconscious thoughts and feelings influence our behaviour. *The concept of the unconscious became the cornerstone of psycho-analysis, referring to a 'system' which is a repository for unconscious thoughts and feelings and to a 'dynamic' process by which thoughts and feelings become unconscious.* (In ordinary speech 'subconscious' is often used to mean unconscious, though psychoanalytical writers only use the term 'unconscious'.) Freud distinguished between material which is 'pre-conscious' and easily brought into awareness, and unconscious material which can only be inferred from our conscious behaviour, usually by someone else a bit detached, in an observing or listening role, as Freud had been when he heard Breuer's story.

Most importantly Freud realised that Anna O, whose disturbance had started when she was nursing her terminally ill father, unconsciously transferred her passionate attachment for her father on to Breuer. Once Freud began his own psycho-analytical treatments of patients he experienced similar reactions from his patients, but unlike Breuer he was not frightened off, and neither did he attribute such feelings to his irresistible charms. Freud thus came to understand and develop *the concept of transference by which patients transfer unconscious conflicts on to the relationship with the doctor, who unconsciously can represent current or past figures from the patient's life. However, the patient experiences their feelings toward the doctor as entirely appropriate to the present and to the particular relationship with the doctor. Transference is not just a passive experience but it can include subtle and unconscious attempts to 'manipulate or provoke situations with others which are a concealed repetition of earlier experiences and relationships'* (Sandler, Dare and Holder, 1973).

I would like to give an illustration of transference from an initial interview with an 81-year-old woman, Mrs Crawford, who had developed various physical symptoms connected with her throat and difficulties in swallowing. There had been exhaustive investigations but no physical cause could be established, so her doctor had suggested some counselling. Mrs Crawford told me of many losses she had suffered, including the deaths of two husbands and a daughter in the Second World War. In addition, she had foot and leg injuries which made it painful for her to walk. She then told me of one of her experiences during the war in which she had seen a little girl suffering from multiple wounds all over her body. When a doctor tried to pick the little girl up, she screamed because of the pain. As the interview proceeded I could see that Mrs Crawford did not want counselling, though I left it with her to contact me again if she changed her mind. I did not hear from her again. I think Mrs Crawford's story about the little girl was a message about the transference to me as a doctor in which she was telling me that her emotional wounds would be too painful to address in counselling.

Freud developed the technique of *free association* by which he asked the patient to say whatever occurred to him. At first, Freud thought that transference was an obstacle to his therapeutic work. However, when of one of his patients, 'Dora', walked out of the therapy prematurely, he realised he had not fully understoond the transference and that instead of an obstacle it is 'our greatest ally'. Freud identified a 'positive' transference, frequently a part of the early stages of therapy, in which everything goes swimmingly between patient and therapist, sometimes with signs of the patient feeling better. A 'negative' transference can soon follow, or even precede the positive feelings and can be manifest in unco-operative and even hostile attitudes toward the therapist and the therapy. He thus recognised a fundamental and often unconscious ambivalence in personal relationships revealed by transference, in what can be abrupt and puzzling swings of feelings like love and hate for the same person. He pointed out that psycho-analysis does not create transference, but merely reveals it as part of any relationship.

Freud was aware that the analyst also transfers feelings on to the patient, a process again unconscious, which he called counter-transference. He saw this as an obstacle to analytical treatment and a powerful reason why analysts should themselves be analysed. Just as the thinking about transference developed, so later workers, particularly Heiman in 1950, have developed the concept of counter-transference. Heiman saw counter-transference as all the feelings stirred in the analyst by the patient, and this was less an obstacle and more an important communication from the patient about the nature of their transference on to the therapist. Personal therapy or counselling is essential for enabling a therapist or counsellor to understand and disentangle their own transferences on to the patient from unconscious feelings communicated by the patient within the counter-transference.

An illustration of a counter-transference communication comes from my work with a carer called Josie. Josie was caring for an elderly woman who suffered from a severe muscular neurone disease which rendered her completely helpless and unable to speak. A friend of the patient complained that Josie had treated the patient roughly when putting her into a wheelchair. The friend had taken her complaint to the hospital manager and Josie had not been present. Josie felt angry, humiliated and shamed, without a chance to speak up for herself. I said to Josie that this was the position of her patient who could no longer speak or do anything for herself. The friend had to speak for her. I talked about how humiliating and frustrating it must be, at an advanced age, to be reduced to the state of a helpless baby, and to have intimate physical activities, like bathing and toileting, performed by others.

Unconscious phantasy and the internal world

I would like now to turn to the work of Melanie Klein and her followers. Klein was inspired by Freud and innovated psycho-analytic work with very young children, which led to important developments in psycho-analytic understanding. Forty years after Freud heard Breuer's story, Klein developed a play technique for children in 1923 which is still used by contemporary child psychotherapists. Faced one day with an 'unresponsive and silent' seven-year-old girl, Klein who was working at home, went into her own children's nursery and gathered some toys for her. The girl at once began to play. Klein was able to understand the unconscious meaning of the play by listening as she would to an adult patient's free associations and by thinking of the symbolic meaning of the play in the way Freud understood dreams and their unconscious meaning.

From her work with children and adults Klein discovered that what is transferred on to the relationship with the therapist are some of the earliest, infantile feelings associated with the first relationships with mother, father and other siblings. Klein's play technique dramatically revealed a complex unconscious *internal world* peopled with all these important figures. The infant, then the child and later the adult, gradually creates an internal world which is coloured by the infant's or child's feelings about these people, their relationships and by the infant's or child's experiences with them. Feelings which are transferred on to the therapist or counsellor reflect this internal world in all its complexity. Klein's understanding of the internal world and how it reflects and affects psychological development evolved into what is known as a *psycho-analytic theory of object relations*. Central to this theory is the concept of *unconscious phantasy*, which means that figures incorporated into the internal world are unconsciously experienced as concretely existing inside the body. They are described as *internal objects* to distinguish them from mere mental representations in the mind, because they are influenced by our feelings and because they have an actuality and life of their own (Shuttleworth, 1989). The earlier example of Mrs Crawford showed how this elderly woman in a communication about the transference spoke of a little girl inside her who suffered many wounds which she felt would be too painful to be picked up in counselling.

The nature of our phantasies and the internal world they construct is seen to affect the structure of our personality. Consequently, working with phantasy in psycho-analytical therapy or counselling is a means of influencing personal change. In particular, change is facilitated in analytic work by the therapist or counsellor offering *interpretations* of unconscious phantasies and transference phenomena. Interpretations are intended to make conscious what is unconscious. (The spelling 'phantasy' is used to refer to unconscious phantasy to distinguish it from conscious 'fantasy'.) Klein and her followers have drawn special attention to the importance of working through phantasies connected with two fundamental sources of anxieties and defences and with two developing states of mind, present from the beginning of life and throughout the life cycle: the paranoid-schizoid position which refers to persecutory anxieties and an unintegrated state of mind; and the depressive position which refers to depressive anxieties and an integrated state of mind.

The paranoid-schizoid position and projective identification

The infant is seen at first to be in an unintegrated mental and emotional state. He has little sense of time and of course no language with which to think or communicate. His main sensations will be in terms of being mothered, like suckling at the breast, being held, bathed or talked to, with little sense of his own or anyone else's continuity. Klein saw the infant as subject to a basic conflict of instinctual strivings: between life-seeking, loving impulses and destructive, hating ones. This inner conflict, the trauma of birth, other separation experiences and the frustration of bodily needs lead to *persecutory anxieties*.

Under the sway of persecutory anxieties the infant's phantasy is that just as he takes in food from a nurturing breast, or comfort from the arms which cradle him or the voice that soothes him, so he incorporates in his internal world a 'good breast' (which Klein used to stand for all the nurturing experiences). The good breast becomes a good internal object to sustain him against his anxieties and in this way he can feel he is the source of the good feelings. In a similar process, just as he expels waste products of urine and faeces, so his phantasy is that he evacuates his anger, frustration or hatred into a 'bad breast' (which stands for the painful and frustrating experiences) as a bad *external object* (this term emphasises how perceptions of external figures, at first the mother, then others, will be influenced by the infant's feelings).

In phantasy the infant may also expel his good objects in order to keep them safe from a harmful internal situation: for example, when he feels full of rage. He may also incorporate his bad objects, the better to keep them under control. Thus, awaiting the next feed, the infant might hallucinate a good breast feeding him, as can be seen in the infant who contentedly sucks whilst asleep, or he might lose interest, or he might experience his gnawing hunger as a bad attacking breast.

At this stage of development the infant's phantasies relate only to 'part-objects' reflecting his fragmented experiences of mainly his mother's care (where 'mother' refers to the birth mother or the main caretaker). In order to avoid any confusion, to keep the good feelings and experiences as separate as possible from the bad ones, to protect the good internal (part-) objects from the bad and to strengthen himself against his anxieties, the infant's phantasies exaggerate the good and deny any bad qualities of his good objects. In a reciprocal way the phantasies deny any good feelings or experiences with his bad objects and exaggerate bad ones. This exaggeration, or *idealisation,* contributes to a black or white view of the world in which an idealised object can abruptly become a persecuting one. For example, if the infant is kept waiting for the next feed, when the breast finally arrives it may be rejected by a screaming infant who cannot be comforted because of his limited capacities for frustration. The good breast, which in phantasy always comes when he wants it, has turned into the bad breast which always keeps him waiting.

The phantasies of expulsion are the basis of a defence of *projection,* the phantasies of incorporation are the basis of a defence of *introjection* and the separation of the good and bad is the basis of a defence known as *splitting.* The defence of idealisation includes splitting and *denial.* These are all necessary defences for the survival of the infant. *Klein described this stage of infant development as the paranoid-schizoid position, 'paranoid' referring to the persecutory anxieties and projective mechanisms of defence and 'schizoid' to the splitting processes. 'Position' emphasises that these anxieties, defences and unintegrated states of mind can be reactivated at later stages of life, particularly as a result of various kinds of stress.*

The most influential concept which has emerged from Klein's understanding of these processes has been about the nature of the projective defence mechanisms which she called projective identification. She understood that in phantasy this defence involves the infant in splitting off good or bad aspects of himself and projecting them into an external (part-)object, which is then identified with those aspects of the self. Klein saw it as an essentially aggressive attack on that object and an attempt to possess and control it. By the infant linking itself up in this way with an external object, the infant remains merged with the object, denying any separation from it. Again, this is a defence mechanism which can be resorted to throughout life. Kleinian theorists see projective identification as the mechanism which underlies transference and counter-transference.

Klein also elaborated the concept of *envy* as representing a fusion of life-seeking and destructive instincts. Envy expresses the desire for something good and life-sustaining, which when frustrated makes spoiling attacks on the source of goodness. She saw envy as innate, present from the beginning of life and varying in degree between individuals. She distinguished envy from *jealousy* which is a resentment connected with a loving relationship, usually a triangular one in which the loved one prefers another; whereas envy is essentially between two people, though it can be mixed with jealousy. Klein distinguished envy from *greed*, which aims to get as much goodness as it can and may have destructive consequences but, unlike envy, does not aim at being destructive. In phantasy greed is essentially a 'scooping-out' introjective process which may therefore harm and deplete the object, whereas envy is a projective process, splitting off bad parts of the self and expelling them in order to attack and spoil the good object. Envy only attacks the good (Segal, 1973).

A fairly fit 82-year-old woman, Mrs Bennett, was creating havoc on the rehabilitation ward where her husband was being treated for a stroke. She was Mr Bennett's second wife, it was her first marriage, and she had married Mr Bennett when she was 61. She accused the doctor of lying to her, was generally distrustful and made the staff very angry. I was told that everyone was fed up with her. Perhaps not surprisingly, she refused to see me when the staff referred her for counselling. Mrs Bennett had evacuated her anger and frustration 'into' the staff which, together with her suspiciousness, encouraged a persecutory, paranoid-schizoid atmosphere which avoided sad feelings.

Holding and containment

Klein gave us an understanding of the infant's experience before he has thoughts or words. Later psycho-analytic theorists have elaborated the mother's contribution to infant development. Donald Winnicott explained how at first the mother provides ideal caring for her infant because of an innate preoccupation with her infant's needs (for example, almost magically knowing when to present the breast as the infant desires it).

Esther Bick described the importance of the mother holding the infant, not just physically but also holding him in her mind, as a way of giving him the experience of gathering together all the different aspects of himself and focusing his attention. For example, the mother holds the infant in a manner which enables him to suckle at the breast. Bick observed how a bright light, or a voice, will hold an infant's attention and give him the experience, momentarily, of being gathered together. The mother provides the infant with an experience of bounded space: the nipple in his mouth plugs a hole that his empty and open mouth can represent. With repeated experiences of being held physically and mentally by the mother, the infant gradually internalises this capacity for himself which he experiences concretely as his skin holding him. The mother thus enables the infant to develop, inside himself, a sense of an internal space into which in unconscious phantasy he can *introject* (meaning incorporate) internal objects. The mother also gives the infant a sense of an external object which has a bounded space into which he can project his feelings.

Wilfred Bion made a unique contribution to the understanding of the mother's importance as a 'container' for the infant's projections. He described how in ordinary circumstances the infant's projective identification is a means of communication to the mother. Projective identification is not simply a phantasy but, by various means, which we still hardly understand, the infant's projections have an emotional impact on the mother, partly due to her capacity to be affected emotionally, consciously and unconsciously. *By receiving the infant's projected emotional experience, especially the infant's distress or terror, and transforming these feelings with her loving thoughts and actions, the mother gives the infant an experience of containment in which his anxieties are modified and eventually he can take these feelings back, introject them, in a modified form. Containment is a means by which the mother gets to know her infant and by which she helps him to know himself and others.*

For example, when the mother cradles her distressed infant, she contains him by her capacity to feel the impact of his distress without being overwhelmed by it and by thinking, consciously and unconsciously, about him and his distress. With many experiences of containment the infant gradually becomes able to internalise this capacity for himself. He develops a basis for thought and ultimately is able to bear pain by thinking, as he establishes in his internal world a mother who can think with love about him.

A 90-year-old man in long stay care, Mr Robertson, was referred to me because the staff were getting into a lot of conflict with him. It seemed they felt he was excessively demanding. He often called out for them and was impatient if they attended to other patients before coming to him. He was riddled with cancer and two years previously he had been given only six months to live. Betty, who was Mr Robertson's keyworker, told me there were particular problems at night when he seemed to get more anxious and kept his radio on as if to keep himself awake. Recently he had had nightmares which involved fears of falling and fears of drowning. I said I thought he was afraid of dying and he feared if he went to sleep he would not wake up again. I felt he was in a panic about dying. Betty said that he became quite confused and sometimes the words in his sentences were jumbled up. She said the other staff found him a problem when they kept him waiting after he'd called for them. She realised he liked to know when the staff would be coming to attend to him.

She said when she told him just how long it would be before she would be able to come to him, he calmed down. I said I thought his infantile fear was of being dropped and falling to pieces. When Betty told him how long she'd be, he had something to hold on to. He felt she held him in mind. It seemed to me that Betty had intuitively understood her patient's need to be held and when I talked to her about his unconscious fears I aimed to help her in containing these deeper anxieties.

The depressive position, depressive anxieties and manic defences

The mother's holding gives her infant a more secure sense of a good object inside him which is a source of integration and her containment moderates the infant's extreme feelings. Gradually he has less need to idealise his good objects, is less frightened of his destructive feelings and has less need to deny or project them. He thus begins to experience more of himself and gains a more realistic view of himself and others. With his maturing perceptual capacities he is able to recognise whole people, starting with his mother, then his father and other family members. At around seven months the infant begins to realise that the mother who lovingly feeds him is the same mother who sometimes keeps him waiting when he is hungry. He comes to realise too that he is the same person who loves and hates his mother. These developments usher in *depressive anxieties*, so called because of the fear for others if destructive feelings get the upper hand over loving feelings, whereas in persecutory anxieties the primary concern is for the self.

Depressive anxieties are especially provoked by experiences of loss, separation and weaning. When the mother leaves, because of his still limited awareness of time and continuity, the infant can feel that she may never return because of his phantasied attacks on her. Thus he is exposed to feelings of guilt and remorse, suffering for his mother who may be lost or injured and for himself who pines for her. At the same time as experiencing the loss of his mother, he also feels that he loses his good internal object. He can feel his internal world is devastated. He tries more realistically to relieve these anxieties by wanting to make reparation to his mother and faces the task of rebuilding 'with anguish' his internal world (Klein, 1940/ 1975). Because of his concern for his objects the infant wants to spare his mother from the excesses of his instinctual needs and at the same time he keeps an eye out for the consequences of his phantasied attacks on her. When his mother returns with love after an absence, the infant realises he has not damaged her. With repeated good experiences with his mother and others, the infant gets a more realistic view of his aggressiveness and his capacity to repair or restore. Following each experience of loss, by having to reconstruct his internal world, over and over again, the infant develops an enriched and stronger sense of his internal objects and a growing independence from others.

Klein described these developmental struggles as working to achieve a depressive position. She emphasised that reaching the depressive position is not simply a stage of development, but in many respects striving for it is a lifelong task: involving less use of projection and more of introjection, essentially acknowledging more of one's internal world, especially unpleasant aspects of oneself and better aspects of the external world (Hinshelwood, 1989).

An 83-year-old woman, Mrs Ames, was referred to me because she was having panic attacks, especially at night. She had become too frail to live on her own any longer and she was soon to be admitted to 'Part III' accommodation (homes for the elderly which cater for people who are not severely physically ill or highly physically dependent, but who need supervised care). Mrs Ames told me that her husband had died four years earlier. She said she was very attached to him. He was a carpenter and built most of the furniture in their house. She awoke one night to find him dead alongside her in bed. She thought, 'Whatever has become of him!' and she feared she might die too. Mrs Ames said she was the last surviving member of her family. Her father had died also 'quite suddenly', when she was just a girl still at school. The family were then threatened with being put in a home. I said I thought in her panic attacks she relived her husband's death and was in a panic that she would die in the night too; and that she was still grieving a much-loved husband. She responded by saying how helpful her husband had been; he used to help her in the kitchen and she showed me a photograph of them both, a handsome couple. She said she could see that she had been ill since his death. Finally, she talked about going to the nursing home. She had visited it and liked the idea of being there. It was near a weekly 'club' she attended, so she would be able to keep going to the club.

I thought Mrs Ames was struggling with depressive feelings of sadness and sorrow. Her associations to her panics revealed the earlier losses which were revived by the imminent loss of her home: the death of her husband whom she was still grieving and the similarly sudden death of her father. She was thus bringing to the surface her infantile anxieties, showing me that in this old woman there was a little girl who was reminded of her father's death and the threat of being put in a home, which was now really going to happen. Showing me the photograph was also showing me a glimpse of her internal world, of the happy couple she had inside her despite her external losses. With this internal security she was in a position to face the loss of her home and make the best of the move to the nursing home, keeping some links through her club with her previous life.

For the infant coping with depressive feelings is an enormous task and to begin with it means recognising his helplessness and dependency on his mother, his love and hatred of her and his jealousy of others. Accordingly he needs recourse to various defences to protect him from unmanageable depressive pain. Klein called these *manic defences*: they are unconscious and are made use of throughout life. They include the developmentally earlier defences of the paranoid-schizoid position, namely splitting, denial, idealisation and projective identification. These earlier defences are now characterised by a sense of *omnipotence* and they are used in a more integrated way to deny an internal world (sometimes referred to as 'psychic reality'), which contains a good internal object, or to deny any threat of destructiveness to the good object. These defences are also used to deny dependence on an external object, especially to avoid any feelings of guilt and loss. Other manic defences are *control*, which denies dependence but also ensures that the object can be depended upon because it is felt to be under control; *contempt*, as a denigration of the importance of the external object; and *triumph*, in which hatred is turned against the depended on and loved object.

Mr Powell, a 70-year-old man suffered a second stroke and then had to be admitted into long stay care because his wife could no longer look after him at home. Previously a pleasant-natured and popular man, once in long stay he began punching staff and was often verbally abusive to them. He masturbated in public and made sexually provocative remarks to the female staff, admitting to taking pleasure in 'winding' them up. Over and over again he would insist on being taken to the toilet when it was apparent he had no need of it. It seemed unbearable for Mr Powell to face his underlying grief and sorrow about what had happened to him at such a relatively young age. Instead he resorted to contemptuous and controlling behaviour, apparently triumphing over those he had now become so dependent upon.

My aim in psychodynamic counselling

I would like to draw these psycho-analytic concepts together in a formulation of my aim in counselling. A paper by a contemporary psycho-analyst, John Steiner (1989), has been particularly helpful in my thinking about how I use psycho-analytic ideas in my work. In the paper Steiner describes an aim which is 'central' to psycho-analysis and which I believe is central to psychodynamic counselling: *to help the client resolve unconscious internal conflict.* Implicit in this aim is the theoretical view that whatever the problem presented to a counsellor or therapist – be it suffering, distress, mental illness, or wish for growth and development – there is an underlying internal conflict. The client is unable to solve the conflict because it is unconscious and because his capacities are depleted by projective processes. Thanks to transference the unconscious conflict will be re-experienced in the counselling because it is transferred on to the counselling relationship. The counsellor helps the client resolve the unconscious conflict by working it through in the counselling relationship. The working through involves the counsellor offering containment for the client and gradually enabling the client to withdraw his projections from the counsellor. The client is then less depleted by projective identification and has more resources to resolve his conflicts and has a more realistic view of internal and external reality.

Steiner pays special attention to the work of enabling the client to take back the projected parts of himself. Difficulties arise because projective identification can be used to avoid recognising the painful reality of separateness. The working through means helping the client acknowledge his dependence on the counsellor as a container who receives and gives meaning to his projections; and working with experiences of loss and separation from the counsellor, a process akin to mourning. This work therefore involves addressing persecutory and depressive anxieties and their various defences. The work is sometimes made more difficult by 'misrepresentations and perversions of reality' where 'perversion' is used in its original sense of 'turning away from what is good and true' (p. 119), particularly from the truth of separateness.

The specific difficulties in pursuing this working through with the elderly are that they are assailed by all kinds of loss: physical, emotional, mental and environmental. The elderly face a pressing loss of life itself in the encroaching reality of their own death.

Psycho-analytical work with the elderly

Freud, whose extraordinary ability to revise and extend his thinking continued into his eighties until he died, nonetheless maintained that people over fifty years of age were unsuitable for psycho-analytic treatment because they lacked the necessary 'elasticity of mental processes'. It is only in the last few decades that psychoanalysts have embarked on work with the elderly, moving from an interest in middle age to 'older adult' clients in their sixties and seventies, before the onset of 'physical and psychological deficit' (Hildebrand, 1982). More recently, psycho-analytic work has been reported with people in their eighties (Davenhill, 1991), including individual psychotherapy in a geriatric unit (Porter, 1991), consultation to geriatric hospitals (Millar and Roberts, 1986; Miller and Gwynne, 1993; Zagier Roberts, 1994; Hildebrand, 1995) and an observational study of a geriatric ward in a general hospital (McKenzie-Smith, 1992).

Psycho-analytic theorists understand that there are various developmental phases which have to be negotiated throughout life and that if one phase is not successfully completed then there will be difficulties in working through the next one. Thus the work on middle age is especially relevant in understanding the elderly. A key paper by Elliott Jaques (1965) described how a crisis in mid-life is precipitated by the awareness of one's own death. Psycho-analytic work with older and elderly clients has revealed that conscious and unconscious fears about death are a recurring theme. Other problems which are specific to the phases of later life and which need to be understood and worked with are as set out below (these are taken from King, 1980, and Hildebrand, 1982, 1995).

1. Changes in identity connected with feared and actual losses of: sexual potency, work role, children who have left home and physical capacities through illness and ageing, with associated loss of independence and fears of dependency.
2. Difficulties in personal relationships, particularly in a marriage, which may have been obscured by child rearing or other activities of mid-life, but which become more apparent when the children are gone and the couple are alone with each other, facing or in retirement.
3. Reversal of gender role: once the pressure of parenthood is over, men and women when ageing tend to take on the other gender's characteristics. Men become more feminine, having

less need for the pursuit of traditionally masculine activities in providing for the family and they become interested in more sensual experiences, social contacts and community projects. Women tend to become more aggressive and competitive, interested in achievement and managerial or political activities.

4. Sexuality: contrary to popular stereotyping, sexuality assumes greater importance during ageing, with some people remaining sexually active into their nineties. For the elderly, sex is less concerned with mere discharge of tension and more with the expression of feelings and an affirmation of the value of life. The older woman's sexual needs are as strong as the older man's and masturbation remains important longer for women than for men, but older and elderly women's sexual needs tend to be treated less sympathetically.

Hildebrand, who pioneered short-term, 16-week sessions of therapy for older adults, has drawn attention to the greater emotional strength and self-reliance of older people. They are more motivated and can more readily use briefer therapy than younger clients. Having survived many life experiences the older client brings certain resilience and an ability to take a longer perspective. The awareness that time is running out brings a sense of urgency to working on emotional problems.

Ruth Porter, who has written of psycho-analytic psychotherapy with geriatric patients, describes internal adaptations that the elderly have to make which are different from adaptations at other ages. She has found that psychotherapy can help elderly patients make these internal adaptations in five areas: loss, anger, discontinuity (from earlier parts of their lives), disorder and chaos, and sexuality (1991, p. 474).

In working with the elderly there is a tension between keeping in mind an awareness of developmental issues specific to phases of later life and understanding what has been revived from earlier times. I have outlined the contribution of Klein's understanding of the paranoid-schizoid and depressive positions in infantile development because these anxieties and defences are revived throughout life. In particular, Klein emphasised that depressive anxieties are aroused in states of mourning, but also whenever there is an experience of loss or adversity. Following an experience of loss, in the internal world the good internal objects are also lost and felt to be dead or injured. The mourner faces the painful emotional task of grieving the external loss of his loved one as well as the internal reparative work of reconstructing the internal world and all his good objects. If there have been early problems in facing depressive feelings then good objects may not be securely established in the internal world and there may be further problems whenever new experiences of loss, change or adversity are encountered. For example, there may be problems in working through a bereavement because the mourner is unable to grieve or remains stuck in his grief. Mr Powell, who was described earlier and who was provocative and abusive to his carers, is an example of someone unable to grieve the many losses consequent upon his stroke.

Jaques' work on the mid-life crisis is especially relevant to thinking about work with the elderly. His work reveals that an awareness of personal death precipitates a crisis because of the revival of infantile depressive anxieties and his work furthers our understanding of *the unconscious meaning of death*. He shows that if the depressive position has not been satisfactorily worked through then unconsciously death will be viewed in terms of the persecutory anxieties of the paranoid-schizoid position. Jaques describes a patient's dream which he found 'typifies unconscious fear and experience of death', in particular a persecutory phantasy when paranoid-schizoid anxieties are dominant. In the dream the patient was lying dead in a coffin, sliced up though connected with a thread of nerve to her brain and so able to experience everything, knowing she was dead but unable to speak or move (1965, p. 236). I find this image particularly horrifying because it so closely matches the *actual* state of some elderly patients who are immobilised and mute, sometimes experiencing fragmented mental states and also capable of experiencing physical and emotional pain.

Jaques does not describe an alternative view of death which might occur when there are less persecutory anxieties and more tolerance of depressive feelings. However, several writers who worked with clients in their eighties (e.g. Davenhill, 1991) have commented on the theme of loneliness in the elderly. Klein (1963) herself gave a paper about loneliness to an international congress when she was 77, just a year before she died. She wrote of loneliness as an internal state of mind irrespective of whether others are present or not. She linked loneliness to depressive anxieties revived by external losses and the corresponding phantasy of the loss of the internal mother who is felt to be dead, which increases fears of one's own death. A recent paper by a Kleinian analyst, Gabriele Pasquali (1993), echoes this theme in describing how achieving emotional closeness and separateness can lead to a loneliness, 'felt to be without remedy'.

Pasquali writes that whatever hopes may be attached to religious beliefs or life extending through the next generations or one's works, 'death is felt as a void' (p. 187).

I think that depending on whether persecutory or depressive anxieties are uppermost – which will depend on how well these anxieties have been worked through in previous phases of development as well as the external circumstances – the experience of ageing and increasing awareness of death will be unconsciously experienced either as a state of persecution, or as a painful void from which there is no escape. These different views of death may oscillate in the same person from time to time according to their emotional and physical state and the care they receive.

In considering the revival of infantile developmental anxieties in the elderly, it is important to point out a difference between the younger and elderly person: for the younger person, or even a mature adult going through a mid-life crisis, the attainment of a depressive position is associated with real developmental gains such as Jaques eloquently describes in terms of achieving mature creativity in mid-life; but for an elderly person it is a process *in reverse*; achieving the depressive position is associated with loss because of physical and mental decline and eventual death.

Psycho-analytic therapists have drawn attention to the *problems for therapists in working with elderly clients*, especially for younger therapists. Pearl King (1980) has noted how difficult it has been for psycho-analysts, from Freud onwards, to think of themselves as old and to be able to address the problems of the elderly. She has pointed out that whatever the age of the therapist, in terms of the *transference*, the therapist may at one time represent a parent for an older client and at another time their child or grandchild, or the client may reverse roles and place the therapist in their position in relation to their parent or spouse, and so on. There are problems arising from the *counter-transferences* that therapists experience toward elderly clients, especially when they transfer feelings about their own parents on to the clients. Brian Martindale (1989a) has described problems arising from fears of dependency in working with older clients which can involve the therapist's fears of his own ageing parents becoming dependent and the elderly client's own fears of dependency. Such fears can lead to elderly clients being referred from therapist to therapist, and from one institution to another for brief therapies.

When there is an age discrepancy between the therapist or counsellor and elderly client, part of the difficulty comes from the fact that the younger worker is preoccupied with different developmental phases from the older client. They have different 'projects' (Biggs, 1989). The younger person will be more oriented towards external tasks at home or work, establishing and maintaining a family and career, whereas the elderly person becomes more inward looking, recollecting and reviewing life experiences and ultimately preparing for death. In between and overlapping with the experience of the elderly, the older adult, as Hildebrand has pointed out, will be undergoing changes of identity including reversal in traditional gender characteristics and new developments in sexuality. Just as the older or elderly person can find difficulties in adjusting to these developmental issues, so too the younger therapist can have difficulty recognising and working with these issues in his older or elderly client, as they perhaps mirror issues in his ageing parents or as they show him an unwelcome image of his own future.

The term 'physically frail' is a conspicuous euphemism for frightening illnesses like strokes which afflict the elderly. 'Elderly mentally frail' similarly conceals the horror of dementia. Ruth Porter describes difficulties for therapists in working with geriatric patients in facing the clients' changed and damaged external and internal body images, and the consequent fears in the therapist of illness and injury; the frustration for client and therapist of working at a slower pace; and the enduring sense of helplessness and failure about what cannot be done for these very ill clients (1991, pp. 484–6). Most of all, the elderly client reminds the younger worker of the reality of their own ageing and death and thus stirs conscious and unconscious fears of dying in the worker.

BRIEF COUNSELLING WITH THE ELDERLY

Introduction

This chapter is about how I approached some of my first referrals after taking up the appointment in the elderly service. Most of the referrals came from a rehabilitation ward which was situated in the long stay hospital. My contact with the patients was brief, often only one or two meetings, because they were then discharged home or transferred into residential accommodation. Most of these elderly patients were not regarded as psychiatrically ill, but were referred because of ordinary emotional difficulties connected with illness and disability.

I have reported some brief work which was appreciated. Some of the work reported was unwelcome and though I felt the patients and relatives could have benefited from further counselling, they chose not to see me again. I hope the work described here will provide an opportunity to study what can usefully be offered by way of counselling in brief contacts with elderly people and their carers. I hope too it will be an opportunity to think about some of the difficulties in this work. The work illustrates a technique for brief counselling which involves thinking about the transferences and particularly unconscious phantasies stirred in these patients' and carers' internal worlds by physical illness. The transferences were usually not interpreted because it would have been inappropriate to encourage a dependency relationship in view of the brevity of the contact. The work shows how carers, whether professional staff or families, can help their elderly patients, by giving them some time to talk about their feelings and by the carers reflecting on their own emotional reactions as a means of under-standing their patients.

Making a Start

As I describe my first referrals, note what can be overlooked because of eagerness to start seeing patients. Note, too, that providing time and space for these patients' feelings quickly led to the unfolding of bereavement reactions to illness and disability.

My first elderly patient

My first referral followed a visit to the acute ward of a general hospital where I was asked to see an elderly man who was soon to be transferred to the rehabilitation ward. His doctor was worried about this man's depressed mood following recent hospitalisation for a physical illness. I was pleased to be referred someone and to be commencing some 'real' work after having spent several days talking to various members of staff and sitting in at ward rounds and other meetings. I was to see the patient in his single room. His doctor took me in and introduced me. I found a small thin man sitting stiffly in an armchair by his bed. He was fully dressed in a grey suit and looked displeased. The doctor left us. I pulled up another chair, sat down and asked him how he felt about talking to me. He replied straight away that he did not want to see me and he had nothing to say! I think I stayed rather longer and tried to persuade him more than I should have because of my keenness to get on with some client work. But he remained adamant in his refusal to talk. Eventually I left, very disappointed.

Mr Miller

My next referral came from the rehabilitation ward which was located in the long-stay hospital. The staff were concerned about a 76-year-old man, Mr Miller, whose physical condition had deterio-rated very quickly since his admission a few weeks earlier. He was now unable to walk and would be confined to a wheelchair for the rest of his life. He lived with his wife in a small two-storey house and the staff felt he could not accept that he would no longer be able to go upstairs. He was worried about how his wife would cope and that he would be 'totally marooned'.

The ward sister asked me if I would see Mr Miller in a small side room alongside the nurses' office. This was a narrow room with a single bed and locker and just enough space to fit a couple of chairs. When Mr Miller was wheeled in, he towered over me, a large man with swollen legs and bandages showing from under his trouser cuffs. He had a sad expression. I asked him how he felt about seeing me. He seemed pleased and said he was grateful to have this opportunity to talk to someone.

Mr Miller spoke about his house being 'upset' because they had to get rid of two armchairs in the living room on the ground floor to make way for a bed to be brought down for him. I said that I thought *he* was probably upset. He almost laughed in agreement, saying that he supposed 'they' were all upset, especially his wife. Later, he said how he would be lost if it weren't for his wife and he cried. When he had recovered his composure, he went on to say that the physiotherapists said they wouldn't take any responsibility for him if he went upstairs, but he thought he was fit enough. Then he talked about going to see his doctor just a few weeks ago, when he was immediately put into hospital. I felt the force of his shock as he said this. I said he had suffered an awful blow and I thought he was still shocked by what had happened. He heaved a sigh of relief and agreed, saying the doctor said he was in a 'terrible state'. I had the impression Mr Miller had not appreciated how ill he had become and was shocked to be suddenly admitted to hospital.

He looked sad again and said if only he had gone to the doctor twelve months earlier, perhaps he would still be able to climb the stairs. He then described his house in more detail. There were just two rooms on the ground floor, a hall and steps into the garden. He seemed forlorn at the thought of not being able to go into his garden again. I felt upset and asked about the possibility of ramps for the steps so he could go out. He didn't feel confident he and his wife could manage with ramps.

The only bathroom was on the first floor. They had been given a commode but he worried about managing without a bathroom. He talked about getting a stair lift installed, but then said he thought it would take too long. I wondered, to myself, whether he feared he might not live much longer. He asked me if he would be going to the day hospital once he was discharged from the rehabilitation ward. I assured him I understood it was arranged for him. He then asked if the further tests and scan he had had meant that he would be cured? I felt very uncomfortable and said 'We don't know'. I then said he wanted me to understand he hoped he could get better.

He agreed about the hope and I felt he was sad to see that. He said his wife was coming tomorrow. I asked if he would like me to see him with his wife. He was pleased at this suggestion, so I concluded the meeting and made arrangements to see them the following week.

The next week John, the nurse who was Mr Miller's keyworker, was on duty. John told me that Mr Miller was sometimes able to do things for himself, like shaving, but at other times not able to do those same things, especially when he was miserable. I asked John, provided Mr and Mrs Miller agreed, if he would attend my next meeting with them. I explained that I thought it would help him to have a better understanding of Mr and Mrs Miller's feelings. John appeared somewhat bemused, but was agreeable. The couple also agreed and we all met in the side room, almost sitting in each other's laps.

Mrs Miller was well groomed, smartly dressed and looked a little younger than her husband. She smiled and said that her sister had recently joked with her, saying 'You married him for better or for worse', and together Mr and Mrs Miller both said 'and this is the worse'. I felt moved in the presence of a loving relationship. I said Mr Miller was very appreciative of his wife. He talked about how important she was to him and cried. Mrs Miller showed a great sympathy with her husband, talking about how difficult she knew it was for someone like him who had been 'so independent' now to be in this very dependent position. With a sense of resignation she said 'We'll doubtless bark at one another' and added it would be important not to 'bottle things up'. Soon after I drew the meeting to a close. They were both grateful and felt they would not need to see me again. I invited them to contact me if they wished. Mr Miller was to be discharged in the next few days. This meeting finished after half an hour and was shorter than the previous one with Mr Miller on his own, which had been for an hour.

Commentary

Looking back at these first referrals I feel somewhat embarrassed at my eagerness to begin seeing clients because of the way it devalued the importance of thinking about the institution by spending time gathering information to assess how best to work within it (see Chapter 6, Introduction). Yet, some time later, when a trainee clinical psychologist joined me on a placement in the hospital, I was indignant that he seemed to feel the real work had only started the day he saw his first patient. I felt he had dismissed the importance of the other activities, like staff and ward meetings, to which he had been introduced. This kind of patient-orientated view of the work to which I and my trainee were drawn can obstruct thinking about the nature of the referral, about who or what is the underlying problem, as distinct from who or what is presented as the problem. In that first referral on the acute ward, it may have been more helpful to have spent some time with the staff talking about their concern about the 'depressed' patient. Why was it necessary to call in an expert? What might the referral have been communicating about the staff's feelings? What could it mean to this man to have me brought in, to be confronted with 'a shrink'? He may have thought they felt he was going mad.

By the time I saw Mr Miller I had decided that it would be better to try to involve patients' keyworkers (see Chapter 8). Although I felt pleased with the meetings with Mr Miller, I remained disappointed and puzzled by his keyworker's apparent incomprehension when I suggested he attend the meeting with Mr and Mrs Miller. On the one hand John seemed to have noticed how Mr Miller's misery affected his ability to do things for himself, but on the other hand John showed little interest in being involved at the meeting or in later discussions with me. It was as if Mr Miller's misery was handed over to me in the referral so that John, and perhaps the other staff, could remain distant from the grief. Thus my role could be used by the hospital as a way of avoiding emotional contact with the patients. My invitation to John was a challenge to this institutional defence, but it failed.

Looking in detail at the material I am struck that by providing Mr Miller with a space in which he could talk and I could listen and think about his experience, he quickly brought a picture of the 'upset house' and difficult adjustments which were being made to accommodate his disability. I think he was also telling me about his internal world in which he was trying to accommodate his emotional upset, though consciously he located the upset in his house. He laughed with relief when his upset could be acknowledged, but this moment of feeling understood reminded him of feeling helpless and missing his wife. He tried to restore his equilibrium by denying his disability, but then was in touch with his shock at being admitted to hospital. When I could register and articulate the shock, he could acknowledge his 'terrible state' through the words of his doctor. He was then confronted with the sorrow in his thought that if he hadn't denied the state of his illness for so long, he might have been treated successfully. It may be that this thought in which he felt some responsibility for the damaging effects of his illness, protected him from the greater pain of seeing that nothing could have been done to prevent his illness. However, I think it is a reflection, unconsciously, of an internal world which is in a terrible state because he feels his destructive feelings have got the upper hand. I was affected by a sense of devastation and started to think about what he might do in arranging ramps, as if he had no internal resources with which to think. I can now see what was difficult for me to stay with was his despair that nothing more could be done for his physical condition; time was running out and perhaps he would soon die. Though wondering about his anticipation of death, I was unable to speak about it. Perhaps sensing my discomfort he turned to me as a medical authority who could tell him about the day hospital and who would reassure him that he would be cured. I took shelter behind a collective 'we' who did not know.

As far as I understood a recovery was unlikely, but my understanding of the medical condition was paltry and in retrospect it would have been better to say that. I often found it difficult to understand the details of the patients' medical conditions. Instead, I felt impelled to think about the possible emotional meaning of the patients' illnesses, in contrast to the rest of the staff who were preoccupied with the physical state and seemed reluctant to take in the patients' feelings. I thus perpetuated an unfortunate split in which I remained an 'expert' about the patients' emotions but relatively ignorant of their physical illnesses.

Mr Miller's references to his wife seemed a cue that he wanted to include her in the counselling sessions. The second meeting was important in supporting the marital relationship to manage what they called 'for worse'. The marital relationship finds echoes in an internal world, where the primary objects include a couple working together to manage loving and destructive feelings. I feel it was helpful to acknowledge Mr Miller's love and gratitude for his wife, to support the external relationship and to recognise the strength of his loving feelings, when internally he felt so damaged by destructiveness. This also supported his wife's capacities which were evident when she could anticipate that their anger and frustration would need to be expressed in 'barking' at one another. I do not want to suggest an idealised 'Darby and Joan' view of elderly marriages – later material in the book (see Chapter 4) soon dispels any such view – and neither do I wish to suggest that only marital relationships offer such support. I simply want to draw attention to the importance of including family and carers in the counselling and of supporting loving relationships.

Bereavement reactions to illness

In the further illustrations of bereavement reactions, note that shock, denial and sadness were more readily expressed than anger and guilt, which were more usually expressed indirectly. See, too, how the carers can also be suffering grief reactions to the patients' illnesses.

Mr Sewell

The experience of shock is a recurring theme. Another man, Mr Sewell, also in his seventies, whom I saw once weekly for six weeks, told me again and again of the circumstances of the stroke which suddenly brought him into hospital. He had been on holiday with his wife in a hotel in Spain. They were very happy celebrating his retirement. It was like a second honeymoon. He collapsed in the bedroom as they were preparing to go down for dinner, and his wife ran for help. The stroke left him paralysed on the right side of his body. At times his speech was a bit slurred and sometimes saliva dribbled from his mouth. I brought him in his wheelchair from the rehabilitation ward to my office. During the first two meetings he wept profusely and with obvious relief.

At the third meeting, on Mr Sewell's instigation, his wife and son joined us. Mrs Sewell was a glamorous woman, probably also in her seventies, with a blonde coiffure and wearing a white trouser suit. Mr Sewell mentioned his crying in the previous meetings, making a joke about staining the carpet in my room with his tears. He described himself as a 'sad clown'. I said I thought he was broken hearted. He cried again and later his wife cried too. However, she and her son (who arrived late) were uncomfortable when Mr Sewell wept and they found ways of encouraging him to make his usual jokes. He talked about his plans to buy a smaller bungalow which would be more manageable and designed for his disability. But, he wondered, what if he had another stroke; 'it would all be in vain'. I said I felt he was worrying about having another stroke and dying and thinking about his wife who would be left.

The next meeting was with Mr Sewell on his own. He was able to talk about some of the difficulty he experienced in coming to terms with the implications of his stroke. He had made some recovery and could walk a little with assistance of the physiotherapist. He kept asking the staff on the ward how much more recovery he could expect, but he was aware that he was inclined 'to give myself the answer I want'. He imagined his paralysed arm recovering and being able to drive again. At the same time he was trying to make plans for the future which took his disability into account. He was worried that his feelings were 'self-pity'. I talked to him about his sorrow which was part of adjusting to the future.

Before the fifth meeting I was asked to contact Mr Sewell's son on his mobile phone. He told me that Mrs Sewell had been diagnosed with cancer and would soon have to undergo an operation. He and his mother wanted to keep this secret from Mr Sewell through fear of upsetting him. I encouraged them to tell him as soon as possible. Mrs Sewell came to the next meeting where Mr Sewell spoke tearfully about her cancer and his fears for her. I said this was another shock when they had not recovered from the shock of his stroke. At the end of this painful meeting, Mrs Sewell stopped in the doorway and asked me how I managed all this sadness. I was a bit thrown by this question, touched by her concern, but somewhat uncomfortable. She didn't come to the final meeting, Mr Sewell said she had problems with the car, 'three punctures'. He talked about his worries about her cancer and the operation and whether she would survive. He was to go a nursing home while his wife was in hospital and during her recuperation. What was worst for him was an unbearable uncertainty, not knowing what would happen.

Commentary

An important aspect of the counselling role in these meetings is to be able to absorb the shock of a disabling illness, much like the shock of a bereavement. Joan Bicknell (1983) has given a detailed description of the bereavement she saw in families with a handi-capped child. Foremost is the reaction of *shock*, followed by *panic*, *denial* and *grief* which includes *anger* and *guilt*, before there can be any *acceptance* of the tragedy. For these elderly patients there is a grieving for their former able-bodied selves. The parallels with bereavement are close because the illness is a forewarning of death, with a chilling reality: it is not uncommon for stroke patients to suffer multiple strokes and die from them, or for elderly patients to die soon after an admission to hospital. It is important for counsellor and carers to be able to face the reality of the patients' fears of death and particularly for the counsellor to be alert to conscious and unconscious allusions to death. The difficulty for the counsellor is in confronting one's own infantile terror of a parent dying, as well as one's own fear of dying. For the elderly couple there is the related anxiety about who will be left. My impression was that Mr Sewell worried about his wife being left on her own and when she was diagnosed with cancer, he then faced being left without her.

Whether to say or do something which will be upsetting to an elderly patient who is in a vulnerable state is a frequent question. More often than not, family or carers confuse their own upset with the patient's or possibly project their upset into the patient, so it is not clear whether, in the wish to prevent upset, they are protecting the patient or themselves. There is, too, a question of whether, having survived a lifetime of experiences, elderly people need this kind of protection. Certainly, I would not have agreed to be party to concealing information from Mr Sewell because of the dishonesty it would introduce into the counselling relationship and because it would have implied I thought he couldn't take it.

Several times Mr Sewell talked about his worries about his wife handling the car on her own, which was a way he expressed worries about his wife managing without him. The image of the punctured tyres vividly conveyed fears about her state. Of course he was also worried about her managing the practicalities like the car, but it is useful to keep in mind both the external circumstances and the internal states they convey. Unlike Mrs Miller, Mrs Sewell was in no state to manage her husband's anxieties because her emotional capacities had been punctured by her own traumatic diagnosis. With hindsight I think her question to me as she left the room, asking about how I managed the distress, was about how unmangeable she found it. This kind of question, or Mr Miller (see above) telling me at the end of the first meeting that his wife was visiting, are examples of what is sometimes known as a *doorknob communication*, because of the recognition that apparently throwaway remarks, when arriving or leaving a counselling session, nearly always carry an important message.

Mr Sewell used humour in a defensive way, to lighten his grief. A sense of humour is a useful way of coping, of getting through otherwise intolerable difficulties, but like all defences, when resorted to excessively, it can create further problems. Dorothy Judd (1989), in her book about working with a dying child, reports research which showed that families and friends and carers of patients with cancer believed they had to remain 'cheerful, positive and optimistic' in their relationships with the patients. She notes how keeping the hospital atmosphere as 'jolly as possible' may be used unconsciously to suppress angry reactions from the patients and to 'lift' the patients out of their depression. This jollity can create a deeper despair if the patients feel that no one can bear their sad or angry feelings.

I think that Mr Sewell shows how patients can collude in maintaining a jolly atmosphere. I think when he brought humour to the counselling sometimes it prevented him being in touch with his grief and therefore obstructed working through the bereavement connected with his illness. When I did not join in on the jokes and challenged the humour, he expressed relief and sorrow, which led to some movement toward accepting the reality of the losses.

Mrs Hill

Just three months after I had started I had one of the most difficult encounters of my career. I was asked to see an 82-year-old woman, Mrs Hill, who had recovered from a stroke and still managed to live alone in her home owing to regular visiting by her two daughters who lived nearby. She was getting more and more angry with the daughters when they came to help and the situation was becoming intolerable for them all. Her elder daughter, a woman in her late forties, brought Mrs Hill who, a little unsteadily, walked with her daughter's assistance into my office. Mrs Hill was a large rotund woman, with many chins and wisps of grey hair falling around her face, wearing a shapeless cotton dress. Her daughter explained her mother was very hard of hearing and it would be better if she stayed with us. I agreed and started to feel a bit anxious. They sat down and Mrs Hill took out her false teeth and then her hearing aid, complaining that both were uncomfortable.

Whatever I said, however loud I shouted, Mrs Hill seemed unable to hear me. Sometimes she put her hearing aid back in her ear, but it made no difference. She could, however, understand what her daughter said, so with the daughter as a kind of interpreter I asked her to tell me something about herself. She spoke about her husband who had died a few years previously. It was an unhappy marriage; he spent most of his spare time at the pub. She described preparing dinner and then waiting with the girls for her husband to come home to eat it. They waited with some dread because he could be unpleasant. I shouted various questions, but each time she only seemed to hear when her daughter repeated what I'd said.

Almost as an afterthought Mrs Hill mentioned that this was a second marriage. She had first been married just before the outbreak of the Second World War. Her first husband had enlisted and disappeared during the war. She waited for him for three years. He was never found. At the top of my voice I shouted 'I think you feel you've spent most of your life waiting!' Mrs Hill looked blankly at me. I repeated myself trying more loudly, feeling desperate to make myself understood, to no avail. So I asked her daughter to repeat this interpretation, at which Mrs Hill beamed a toothless grin and slapped her thigh with glee, saying to me: 'Now you're talking!'

Later, I added that I thought each time she waited for her daughters to visit she was reminded of the other times when she waited for her two husbands. She returned to talking of her regrets about the marriage to her second husband. She was particularly unhappy about the way he treated her daughters. It seemed he was cruel to them. At this point Mrs Hill's daughter became upset and angry, telling me she didn't want to talk about her father or think about him any more. It was drawing near the end of the hour and I offered to see them again. Mrs Hill looked interested in coming back, but I could see that her daughter did not agree. They did not return.

Fifteen months later I was told that Mrs Hill had suffered a second stroke; she could no longer speak or swallow food and she was to be put into a nursing home. I was asked to see her daughters because the staff on the rehabilitation ward felt they were finding it 'difficult to stand back'. When I saw the daughters they complained bitterly that the doctor on the ward had told them they were 'too tied to their mother and visited too often'. They were very angry. I said that perhaps they also felt angry with me following my meeting with Mrs Hill the previous year. They agreed. The elder daughter said she and her mother were upset for some days after the meeting. She added that there was no point in getting upset, it was all in the past. The younger daughter then talked about her suspicions about the hospital, that they'd had to make frequent visits to keep a check on what the staff were doing. They were unhappy because the staff had 'threatened' to send Mrs Hill to a nursing home and hadn't told them. They emphasised that their mother had had a hard and unhappy life. I said I felt they were trying to make it up to her. They agreed and seemed to soften in their attitude, speaking more calmly and with resignation about the possibility of Mrs Hill going to a nursing home.

Commentary

When Freud's patient Dora, who was 18, broke off treatment prematurely, Freud wrote that her father several times gave assurances that she would return. Freud doubted this because he suspected that Dora's father was only interested in the therapy so long as Freud did what the father wanted, which Freud was not willing to do. As with the young, therapy or counselling with the elderly is often dependent on the co-operation of relatives. Despite her hearing problems I felt I made a good contact with Mrs Hill. I think in my counter-transference I experienced something of how desperate she felt. She was delighted to be understood and eager to talk about her unhappiness. However, it was an upsetting meeting. I think in terms of the daughter's transference to me I became the cruel father inflicting pain on her and her mother. Ironically I was trying to show them that Mrs Hill's anger with her daughters when they visited was the anger transferred onto the daughters about the two husbands who had kept her waiting. In other words, contrary to the daughter's objection that it was all in the past, because of transference onto the daughters the anger and pain was still being experienced in the present. But the painfulness of this exploration evoked a negative paternal transference to me.

I was also puzzled about Mrs Hill only being able to hear her daughter, no matter how hard I tried. I felt I couldn't prise them apart, even when it was clear Mrs Hill wished to return for more counselling and her daughter didn't. Later, the somewhat curious referral from the rehabilitation ward, that the daughters couldn't stand back, seems to reflect something of the same process: they could neither look after their mother any more, nor let her go to a nursing home.

I interpreted the daughter's opening remarks about their anger with the rehabilitation doctor to be an expression of their negative transference to me. This interpretation was confirmed when they were then able to express their anger with me. This is an example of a split transference, in which the client(s), in talking hostilely about some outside person can be splitting off their anger in the transference about the counsellor. The negative feelings need to be gathered into the transference onto the counsellor in order for the ambivalent feelings to be worked through. It is of course tempting for the counsellor to retain this split, and not to have to face the client's anger and apparently be favoured as the good guy in contrast to the baddies elsewhere.

I think the daughters' anger with me, with the doctor (who was female) and their suspicions of staff on the ward were all expressing a negative transference of a father who was trying to prise them apart from their mother. (Different transferences can occur irrespective of the gender or age of the counsellor.) It seems likely to me that

Mrs Hill's second husband, who seemed such a poor husband and father, did not help these girls separate from their mother, or her from them, instead he made them even closer allies against a common enemy, bound together by their anger at his abandonment. My successful interpretation to Mrs Hill threatened this alliance by making a link with her with which she was delighted, but which upset her daughter because at that moment I was coming between them like a father who has a special relationship with a mother. The daughters had separated from their mother and established families of their own. But their mother's deteriorating physical condition, and the increasing reality of her likely death, doubtless revived the daughters' infantile fears of abandonment. Reciprocally, for Mrs Hill the grief about her strokes, the regrets about her married life, the loss of her home and the imminence of death, very likely led her to cling to her daughters as a life raft and to hear only her daughter's voice. When I could acknowledge the daughters' loving and reparative feelings, that they were trying to make it up to their mother, it supported their adult concern for their mother and seemed to help them accept the plans for her future care.

3

OPEN-ENDED COUNSELLING WITH THE ELDERLY

Introduction

This chapter describes two clients who engaged in open-ended counselling work. When I started at the hospital the clinical psychology manager agreed that I could take on some clients for open-ended work to help me gain a deeper understanding of elderly people. The clients were seen in my office in the long-stay hospital. The chapter illustrates some of the issues which emerged from a longer therapeutic contact, especially feelings about ageing and the inevitability of death. I think these elderly people sought counselling because the awareness of death made it urgent to sort out some difficult emotional issues before they died.

Mrs Taylor: An elderly woman waiting for death

I begin with a description of work with an elderly woman covering 16 weekly counselling sessions, including the last two which took place in hospital, a fortnight before she died. It is an account of a woman who seemed, in remarkable ways, to have remained strong and fit until she was in her eighties and then suffered a sudden physical decline. I have given excerpts from the sessions which show an awful dilemma: life had ceased to hold any purpose for this woman and she was impatient to die, but at the same time she feared death. Counselling seemed to be the *only* opportunity she had to talk about these feelings and yet she had been an in-patient and an out-patient in the general hospital and attended a day centre for the elderly. I think her feelings are shared by many elderly people who could benefit from opportunities to discuss their feelings with friends, relatives and carers.

Referral and the assessment meetings

> Note problematic aspects of the counselling, beginning with the way the referral was accepted, and the assessment meetings, in which I was drawn into an infantilising attitude towards this elderly woman.

Mrs Taylor was 80 years old. She was referred by a consultant physician from the general hospital who told me Mrs Taylor had recently been discharged from the acute ward where she had been admitted suffering from shingles, nausea and renal failure. There had been a fracas on the ward when her son had threatened the female consultant physician. Apparently he lived underneath his mother in a house which was divided into two flats. The consultant was worried about the relationship between mother and son. Mrs Taylor, who had been very active and out each day in the local shopping centre, was now 'hesitant and shaky'. She would certainly not be able to resume her active life. She was to return for an out-patient appointment during which the consultant intended to refer her to me. I was informed of arrangements which could be made for her to have transport to bring her to see me. I gave the consultant an appointment to pass on to Mrs Taylor when she saw her. The appointment was subsequently cancelled because Mrs Taylor was re-admitted to hospital.

I did not hear again until five months later when Mrs Taylor's GP contacted my secretary and asked if she could be given another appointment. Mrs Taylor attended this appointment with her daughter-in-law. She came into my office shuffling in tiny steps, leaning heavily on her daughter-in-law's arm. It was a cold wintry day in late February and she was wearing a long grey overcoat with large buttons all the way down. She stood struggling to unbutton the coat and looked appealing for help to her daughter-in-law, who appeared exasperated and reluctantly assisted with the buttons. Mrs Taylor sat down breathless. She was a slight figure, with thinning grey hair curled at the ends. She had rather large spectacles, bright eyes and was neatly dressed in a skirt, blouse and cardigan. Her daughter-in-law sat alongside her making a sharp contrast, a tall angular woman with reddish hair, who, in a business-like manner, introduced herself and asked me if she could speak with me alone. Mrs Taylor remained silent. When I asked her about my seeing her daughter-in-law, she answered in a tremulous voice that she had no objection. So I agreed, saying that I would also like to see Mrs Taylor on her own after I had spoken with her daughter-in-law.

Once on her own the daughter-in-law launched into a tirade of complaints about Mrs Taylor. She said there had been a great change since her mother-in-law's illness because she had become frightened and dependent, a burden on her and her husband, who was Mrs Taylor's only son. Their life was now terribly constricted since Mrs Taylor wouldn't let them go anywhere without her. Furthermore, she suspected her mother-in-law of malingering because she would tell them she couldn't do anything for herself but they could hear her moving around quite agilely upstairs. When they appeared she would be on her sofa saying she couldn't move. She said her mother-in-law had a different story for everybody.

I found this an extremely difficult interview; it was hard to stop the flood of complaints and I felt overwhelmed with the daughter-in-law's rage, almost suffocated by her.

When I saw Mrs Taylor she said she didn't mind talking to me. She said she had suffered badly with shingles and showed me where the shingles had affected her around the neck. She was very upset about feeling so weak and helpless, but she couldn't see how I could help her poor physical state. I agreed that there wasn't much I could do about her physical illness, but said it could be helpful to understand more about her feelings and how they might contribute to her physical difficulties. She seemed interested. I asked her about her life. She said little about herself, except that she'd had a good childhood and a poor marriage, but she didn't want to talk about her marriage.

At the end of these interviews I felt perplexed and still affected by the daughter-in-law's suffocating rage. I said that before I could make any recommendation about what might help, I would like to meet Mrs Taylor's son.

A fortnight later Mrs Taylor's son and daughter-in-law came to see me. I felt some apprehension after what I had heard about his threatening behaviour to the consultant. He was a thick-set, intense man, in a black suit and carrying a black leather briefcase. But he was mild mannered and eager to talk about the problems with his mother. He told me his father had died 26 years ago and he had left home shortly after, though later he built a house for himself with a floor for his mother. He said that until her illness his mother had been caring, independent and likeable. She had often done the shopping for them and other household chores like washing and gardening. Now she was very dependent, couldn't be left on her own and claimed not to be able to do anything. She seemed to feel too frail to lift a spoon, whereas once she had been formidable. She had run a factory, could do any manual job in it and used to lift heavy equipment. Even up to her eighties she was extremely active and looked younger than her years. After two strokes, she had managed to make a full recovery and resume life to the full.

As they talked, I again found the atmosphere of rage and persecution intolerable. I struggled to think and finally said I thought that Mrs Taylor appeared to have been quite an exceptional woman who had defied ageing, but now age and illness had caught up with her and perhaps she and they were afraid of her dying. The effect of this interpretation was like suddenly releasing air from a balloon; the tension dissipated. I felt I could bear to be in the room again and they both visibly relaxed a little. The further effect of the interpretation was that they brought new and important material. Mrs Taylor's daughter-in-law told me that her mother-in-law had had a fiancé, Jack, who had hung himself because he had tuberculosis and Mrs Taylor had found him. Jack had given her an engagement ring which she had never removed until this latest time she was in hospital.

At the conclusion of this interview I offered to see Mrs Taylor for once-weekly individual counselling of 50-minute sessions, provided she agreed. I proposed meeting her for the next three weeks until my Easter holiday and to hold a review after Easter to see if she wanted to continue. Her daughter-in-law said she was willing to bring her each week.

Commentary

In offering the consultant an appointment to give to Mrs Taylor I was drawn into a somewhat infantilising and controlling attitude. Instead, I could have asked Mrs Taylor to contact me for an appointment if she wished to pursue counselling, which would also have given some indication of her motivation. I was guilty of perpetuating an infantilising attitude by treating her like a young child who had to wait outside while I talked to her daughter-in-law. Though a separate interview was requested by the daughter-in-law, my acquiesence led to an enactment of the very problems she complained about because we were both acting as if her mother-in-law was unable to to take part in an adult conversation. Excluding Mrs Taylor from the subsequent meeting with her son and daughter-in-law continued this enactment. Looking back I can see that another aspect of this infantilisation is an expression of rage against a mother who becomes like a dependent child and who can mother no longer. This rather exceptional woman had looked after her son and daughter-in-law like a live-in housekeeper. They were furious and disbelieving that she could not continue doing so. To exclude her from these meetings was to collude in an attack on her adult self by only seeing her as a dependent child and to avoid the pain of thinking about an adult woman who suffered the humiliation of being reduced to a child-like state.

Infantilisation of the elderly, embarrassing to see in myself and all too common in my experience of carers, is a form of defensive splitting in which the patients are treated as children so the staff can be adults. An alternative and complementary split that also occurred was where the staff tended to see themselves as young and the elderly patients as old and rather undifferentiatedly old. For example, staff were often surprised when I asked *how* old the patients were. These splits keep staff and patient separate and remove the staff from worries arising from feeling more identified with the patients, especially fears that as they age, one day they too might suffer these debilitating illnesses. Infantilisation of their elderly patients removes the staff from their infantile terror of a parent dying and from facing their own mortality.

The suspicions that Mrs Taylor was lying about her disability avoided the pain of acknowledging the frightening implications of her illness. I did not take up the son and daughter-in-law's anger with her in an interpretation. In retrospect I think it was as well that I didn't because such an interpretation could have felt persecuting and contributed to an avoidance of deeper pain. But in the interpretation I offered, when I got hold of the anxieties about Mrs Taylor dying, particularly the infantile fears of a mother dying, there was a visible reduction of tension. They were more able to be in touch with their adult selves and think about Mrs Taylor. Thus more useful information emerged. Some light was shed on why the anticipation of dying might be an especially difficult experience for Mrs Taylor because of the tragic suicide of her fiancé. I then felt I had a basis on which to proceed. However, my interview with Mrs Taylor had not been too promising, so it felt better to make a tentative arrangement which would allow her and myself to see if counselling could be helpful to her.

I wonder now whether it would have been useful to have suggested meeting Mrs Taylor with her son and daughter-in-law; or suggested the son and daughter-in-law met with another counsellor or therapist, to work in parallel with, and thereby support, my counselling of Mrs Taylor. At the time I had the impression that they would not have joined in further meetings. I felt that Mrs Taylor needed something private for herself on her own. But I think I could have questioned the arrangement for the daughter-in-law to bring her each week and encouraged separate transport to give Mrs Taylor more independence and choice about attending the sessions.

The first three sessions

> The early sessions include a procedure often used by counsellors: a trial period of counselling to allow more time for an assessment of the client and to explore the feasibility of offering longer work, which enables client and counsellor to make a more informed choice, but also needs monitoring for the feelings such a procedure stirs in the client.

At the first session Mrs Taylor shuffled somewhat breathlessly into the room. I decided not to assist her in walking and simply to wait. But as she struggled to undo the large buttons of her grey overcoat I felt impelled to help her with them and hung the coat for her. She thanked me for seeing her. I explained about meeting for the next three weeks and then reviewing the situation after Easter. I said the counselling was an opportunity to talk about whatever she wished and that it could be helpful to bring any dreams if she remembered them. She then told me she had been incontinent, that she had no strength and couldn't get a grip on things. She became upset as she told me about how lonely and inactive she felt, spending much of the time on her own except for going three days each week to a day centre for the elderly.

Mrs Taylor said she felt hurt because her son was not affectionate to her. She would have liked him to kiss her and hold her hand. Then she talked of Jack, whom she knew in her early twenties and to whom she had felt very close, but he died from tuberculosis. Later, when she was 29, she married her husband, Bill, and he died when she was in her fifties. I saw a flash of her wit as, with a twinkle in her eye, referring to her marriage she quipped, 'a late start and an early finish'. Bill was a heavy drinker and to her shame he was frequently 'incontinent', wetting their bed. She felt angry and hurt. I wondered to myself whether her husband felt she loved only Jack.

In the second session Mrs Taylor told me of another man, Tom, who had been her fiancé. He became depressed because he lost his job. He had taken poison and then cut his throat. He was found dead on a path which was their favourite walk. Her hands shook as she spoke of this tragedy. I felt somewhat confused because of the slightly different account her daughter-in-law had given me in which Jack and Tom were fused together. When I asked about Jack, Mrs Taylor said she had known him before Tom, but because of his illness they could only be friends. After he knew he was dying from tuberculosis he gave her some money to buy a piece of jewellery to remember him with. She bought a diamond ring which she wore on her little finger.

In the third session Mrs Taylor went over some of this history again. I ventured an interpretation that she felt guilty and responsible for the deaths of the three men who had been close to her. She looked rather quizzically at me and said no, she didn't think she felt like that.

Commentary

I can see from the start I felt in the grip of a dilemma of how much to help Mrs Taylor as she entered the room. Whilst I didn't feel I needed to assist her walking, I couldn't stand by and not help her as she struggled to unbutton her coat. There remained doubts in my mind whether these were genuine difficulties or attempts to manipulate me. On these and other occasions I felt I might be suspicious and punitive like her son and daughter-in-law by not helping her, or manipulated and foolish if I did. This counter-transference may have picked up some of Mrs Taylor's own dilemma of not knowing which way to turn: whether to allow herself to collapse into helplessness or to struggle to continue to be independent.

The early sessions were time for her to settle in, though it was difficult starting with just three weeks before a holiday. I was impressed that she was soon able to tell me about her husband in spite of her shame, but I think I became rather incontinent in an ill-timed interpretation about her guilt. It would have been better to have offered some understanding of her feelings about having to come for counselling: her sense, perhaps, that she was being emotionally incontinent by needing to talk about her feelings; and that needing counselling was a reflection of her loneliness, there was no one else she could talk to about her unhappiness. I think, too, that she was probably wary of starting to depend on me because I was soon to abandon her during my holiday, reminiscent of how she had been let down by other men in her life. Although the arrangement to have a review after the Easter holiday gave her the choice of whether to continue with me or not, she could have felt it was an opportunity for me give up on her.

I thought that ageing and death were especially frightening to Mrs Taylor because of the earlier traumatic deaths in her life and that she had managed to defend herself against these fears by exceptional energy and youthfulness. Her sudden physical deterioration had broken through these defences and revived memories of earlier losses. The shingles circling her neck suggested an unconscious revival of the feelings about the suicide of her fiancé who had cut his throat. I thought counselling could help her digest the earlier anxieties which I hoped might enable her to come to terms with ageing and the anticipation of her own death.

Following the Easter break

Note that as the work progressed Mrs Taylor was able to express more of her anger. But note also my difficulty in taking up her angry feelings in relation to myself in the transference.

Mrs Taylor came back saying she had nothing to talk about, she'd told me everything. Then, in exasperation, she held up her hands, saying they shouldn't be soft and clean like that. She used to do all the gardening and the washing and ironing. Now she was frightened to be left alone at night and was a burden on her son and daughter-in-law. She lay on her sofa every day, exhausted and breathless, unable to do anything. She had no energy and felt tense all the time, not knowing what she was tense about.

I asked about her parents and her family life. She brightened up a bit as she talked about her mother who was generous and kind and whom she cared for when she was dying. Her mother lost her memory, could not walk and was incontinent. Mrs Taylor brought her mother home and slept on a day bed in the same room with her. It meant that her son, who was 15 at the time, didn't have a room of his own because he had to share with his father. She felt she neglected him and he resented it. Her father had died some years before and she had been very attached to him. Towards the end of the session I raised the question of how she felt about continuing counselling. She said she felt I was the only one she could speak to about these matters and she wanted to continue. I agreed that we could meet for as long as seemed useful. I said she or I could raise the question of finishing for us to discuss and hopefully agree about, but whenever we decided to finish it would need some time, at least a month's notice, to work on together.

At the following fifth session, Mrs Taylor complained of finding it harder to walk. She brought a dream in which her mother and father were quarrelling because they had no money. She offered to give them some of her money but she found she had none. She went upstairs to see if she could find any and saw her old friend Mabel ill in bed, being looked after by another friend Dorothy. When I asked Mrs Taylor what the dream reminded her of, she talked about times when she had no money. She didn't borrow any because it wasn't done then, not like now when people have it so easy. Her friends Mabel and Dorothy used to work together in a factory with her. In an interpretation about the dream I picked up the anger in the quarrel and talked about her anger about feeling so depleted. She then spoke of the problems with her heart and kidneys, and that she was too old for dialysis because it needs to be given to the youngsters. Rather sorrowfully, she said nothing could be done about her heart.

Mrs Taylor then recalled my talking about her resentful feelings about not being able to do anything. Looking distressed, she said a few days ago she was nasty to her brother and sister when they came to visit her. They had been away at a seaside town where she used to go with them when she had been well. She'd scolded them, saying, 'You've been gadding about, not bothering about me!' She said she felt so resentful about so many things, repeatedly asking herself 'Why has this happened to me?' I said I felt she was waiting to die, to which she quickly replied 'God will take me when He's ready.' I thought she felt God was punishing her by keeping her waiting and she was tormented with questions about why He did so. Mrs Taylor said she did not fear death but more the way she might die. She worried that she would become more physically disabled and suffer a slow death.

In the sixth and seventh sessions Mrs Taylor continued to express an intense anger about what had happened to her. Her breathing difficulties also increased and sometimes appeared in the sessions when she would have to stop talking and seemed to be gasping for breath, though she soon recovered. Much of her anger was directed against her son and daughter-in-law because they kept insisting that she should be more independent. But she understood from the doctor that she wasn't going to get any better. She was regretful about being a burden on them and began to see that her resentment made them resentful. I said that her fears about being left alone prevented her son and daughter-in-law from going out on their own and kept them in the house just as she was confined in it. She replied that she didn't mean to put a 'stopper' on their lives, it wasn't deliberate. They spent less and less time with her and she was furious because she felt they kept fobbing her off with stories about how busy they were in order to avoid being with her. There were plans for them to take her away for a weekend with an old friend of hers she had not seen for a very long time, but at the last minute the son cancelled the plans because of work. She was terribly hurt. I felt angry and sorry too.

Commentary

The Easter holiday break brought a strong negative transference into the counselling relationship, which was helpful because it enabled Mrs Taylor to express some of her rage and frustration. For a while my difficulty was in gathering up these angry feelings in relation to myself in the transference. For example, unconsciously she felt I had been gadding about during the holiday, like her brother and sister, with no interest in her and that, like her son and daughter-in-law, I did not want to spend time with her. Mrs Taylor's envy of me was appropriate because, unlike her, I could come and go. Ruth Porter, who has written of individual psycho-analytic psychotherapy with elderly patients, points out the need to recognise 'envy that is appropriate to the therapist' (1991, p. 485) because the therapist is mobile and independent. Angry or envious feelings are not easily expressed by someone who is weak and dependent, and neither are such feelings welcome in most professional care settings or amongst families. But it is important for elderly clients to be able to express anger because, as Porter has pointed out, unexpressed anger can have damaging effects on the internal world and can inhibit mourning and forgiveness, whereas when anger is expressed it can often bring about constructive results, especially if there are justified complaints, thus 'reinforcing hope and counteracting help-lessness' (p. 477).

Faced with Mrs Taylor's anger and envy, it was tempting to perpetuate a split transference by not drawing the anger on to myself so that I could remain a good object, a nice counsellor, in contrast to the others whom she riled against. My interpretation of the dream about her anger made way for some sorrowful feelings to emerge connected with her heart which nothing could be done about (perhaps a reference to her loving feelings which may have felt so injurious to the men in her life). But when I did not link her angry feelings with myself in the transference, I failed to take up her immediate worries about the damaging effects of her destructive feelings on her relationship with me.

I took some of the sessions, including her dream, to supervision. My supervisor drew attention to Mrs Taylor's infantile fears in the dream, that she was trying to put it right for mummy and daddy but felt she couldn't; and that she felt like a child asking where do the good things come from, a child who was asking for more because she was so frightened she would not get enough, manifest in her gasping for breath. She felt a helpless little child who feared nobody loved or wanted her, and her adult self was also in a rage about being reduced back to a child-like condition. My supervisor drew my attention to Mabel and Dorothy in the dream, signalling Mrs Taylor's longing for some contemporaries, most of whom of course were dead, and that she felt that when I saw her, unlike a friend, it was because it was my work. The supervision helped me to think about the negative transference expressed in the rage about her son and daughter-in-law and supported me in gathering these feelings into the counselling relationship. The importance of working with these negative feelings in the transference was to relieve Mrs Taylor's external relationships from those feelings.

The last months

The final period of the counselling includes a summer holiday and a change of session time and therefore illustrates some of the feelings about separation and loss which are galvanised by breaks or changes in sessions. The last sessions at the hospital bedside show fears of death, in both the client and myself, and the value in talking boldly about death.

Over the next few weeks a pattern emerged in the sessions. Mrs Taylor would arrive walking with great difficulty, and looking more and more drawn and dishevelled. Sometimes her hair was obviously uncombed and on one occasion there was a food stain on her blouse. She would sit down gasping for breath, but after a few minutes she would regain her composure and was clearly pleased to be with me.

I vividly recall her describing a lunch at the day centre where they had served up a vegetable pie and included the same vegetables in the pie as side vegetables. I could see she felt anything could be served up to the old folk who wouldn't know the difference. I interpreted negative feelings more consistenly in the transference. But she was usually reluctant to think that she had any negative feelings towards me, seeming to need to preserve me as an exclusively good object and unable to bear a more ambivalent attitude.

By now it was early summer. There were some lovely moments of contact between us when she would pause as some late sunlight entered the room, listening to a bird that sang on a rooftop nearby. She recognised it as a blackbird, a bird she was particularly fond of. I have little knowledge of birds and was pleased to learn about the blackbird and enjoyed the birdsong with her. However, I was troubled by Mrs Taylor's worsening physical condition. Though she had been seen by her GP, little seemed to have been done for her. I spoke with the consultant physician again to gain some more clarification of Mrs Taylor's state of health. The consultant confirmed that Mrs Taylor was in a genuinely poor physical state but she was still puzzled why Mrs Taylor was quite so weak.

At the end of June, in the twelfth session, Mrs Taylor told me her son and daughter-in-law had arranged a two-week summer holiday during which she was to be resident in a local nursing home, in the last week of July and the first week of August. I told her I would be away for the month of August. A week later I had to re-arrange the day of the session a fortnight ahead. In the rest of the session she was very angry, describing herself as 'an old rag' and an imbecile because of the way her son and daughter-in-law kept things from her. I took up her rage with myself who didn't tell her why there had to be a change of day for the session ahead, or about my holiday. I said that she suspected I wanted to get away from an old rag. She replied with a sparkle in her eye and a smile, 'Whether you like it or not I'm coming!'

Mrs Taylor's anger increased. In the thirteenth session she said she'd had a row with her son. In the fourteenth session she came in a fragile state, so much so that, unusually, her daughter-in-law stayed in the waiting area while her mother-in-law was with me. The next session was the one I had rescheduled for a different day. Mrs Taylor did not turn up. I had a message that she had been admitted to the general hospital. I learned that she was admitted because she was in a weak state. The following week I sent a message that I would visit her at the usual time and day of her session.

On my way to see her I spoke to the nursing staff. They seemed surprised that Mrs Taylor was still alive, but they couldn't understand why she had come back into hospital because she looked no worse than before. Mrs Taylor had a single room. When I entered she was sitting up in bed, supported by several pillows and with an oxygen cylinder and mask alongside her. I sat in a chair beside her bed. She closed her eyes, remained silent and seemed to be trying to fall asleep. I felt I was being given the cold shoulder, but I wondered too if my presence meant she felt more comfortable and then could allow herself to sleep. Then I became preoccupied with watching her breathing, fearing she might die at any moment. I talked to her about her anger with me for changing the session time and for leaving her during my holiday. I said that getting herself admitted to hospital ensured she would be looked after 24 hours a day in contrast to my inadequate care. She looked interested in the interpretation, but then closed her eyes. I started worrying about her breathing, again fearful she might die. I also had a fantasy that she was deliberately holding her breath. I talked about her fear that she might die, and linked it with her feeling that I was dropping her by leaving her. She again told me God would take her when He was ready. But this time she added that nobody had come back from the grave to say what it was like. During the silences which followed I was uncomfortable to find myself thinking about what I would do with her session time if she died. So I said that she might feel I was waiting for her to die so I could get on with something else. She said she was waiting and wondering, but she did not say more about what she meant.

The next week was the final week before my holiday. Mrs Taylor was still in hospital and I went to see her at the usual time. Apparently there had been no change in her condition. When I arrived she was sitting up in bed watching television. Almost reluctantly she turned the television off and looked at me. For some time she said nothing. I noticed she was breathing in very short breaths in a panicky way. I talked to her about her panic that she would die. She tended to lapse again into silence, still breathing in short breaths. Only towards the end of the session did she give some acknowledgement of the interpretations, with some humour saying she had moaned at me about my holiday. She also commented on the way the furniture had been placed in the room (a wardrobe that hadn't been centred properly and floor tiles which had been inexpertly laid). With some pride she told me she wouldn't have done it like that.

She had a plate of sandwiches in front of her and explained that she hadn't eaten them because her son was bringing some special food which her daughter-in-law had prepared for her. Just as we were near the end of the session she looked at me rather mischievously and took a bite from one of the sandwiches. I said I felt she didn't think much of what I'd offered her today, the sandwich was a better bet. Her eyes lit up, she smiled and said 'Well, there's the door!' It was nearly time to finish, I reminded her when I would resume after the holiday and bade her farewell. When I returned from holiday I learned that Mrs Taylor died in hospital, a fortnight after I last saw her. I was shocked and very sad. I wrote to her son and daughter-in-law to express my sorrow, offering to see them if they wished. They did not reply. I missed seeing Mrs Taylor for a long while after.

Commentary

It seemed to me Mrs Taylor got into an increasing panic about dying. She may have been particularly frightened of dying alone during her son's holiday which overlapped with mine. I think when she felt I understood some of her fears her panic temporarily subsided and she was able to breathe normally and enjoy the blackbird's song. But the change of session time and the approach of the summer holiday, like the Easter break, undoubtedly revived anxieties about being abandoned and a lot of rage.

The reason for not disclosing information about the change of session time or about my holiday was to to keep some space to understand the conscious (and especially the unconscious) phantasies that were stirred by these events. There is no golden rule about whether to offer explanations or not, except keeping the interests of the client in mind. It is important to be aware of wanting to avoid a client's anger by offering a good excuse. Even if an explanation is offered, it does not mean that a client will not have feelings and phantasies which need to be explored, though because there is an explanation it may be more difficult to do so. Awareness of feelings stirred by holidays or changes in arrangements is important for counsellors and also carers, as they come and go in the lives of their elderly clients.

During the last two sessions in hospital, which were the final weeks of Mrs Taylor's life, her remoteness from me can be understood as a form of 'anticipatory mourning' as she prepared to die. Dorothy Judd, when writing of her work with a dying child, describes anticipatory mourning (citing work by Eissler) as a process in which someone who is dying 'gradually detaches from his loved ones as a way of easing separation before death' (p. 147). Judd points out that because family and relatives have a strong wish for the patient to survive, a therapist may be in a better position to allow this process of anticipatory mourning to happen and the transference relationship can be 'a substitute arena for the relinquished ties' (p. 147). Another aspect of my fears about Mrs Taylor which Judd's work illuminates is her understanding that for those involved with the dying together with the conscious feelings of guilt and failure, there are also 'primitive phantasies' of unconscious impulses of hatred towards loved ones from early life, which can lead to feelings of being responsible for the death. Hence my panic at Mrs Taylor's bedside doubtless reflected underlying phantasies in which I felt I would bring about her death.

Mrs Taylor seemed to feel quite persecuted by her loneliness. But I felt in the moments of closeness she shared with me that her loneliness became more sad; as Gabriele Pasquali (1993) describes it, 'a loneliness felt to be without remedy'. But as her physical frailty worsened I think there was an increase in anxieties about angry and destructive feelings taking over in her internal world and diminishing her good internal objects. These anxieties seemed to be concretely experienced in fears of losing her breath, the breath of life. Thus there seemed an oscillation between persecutory and depressive fears of dying. When I could gather her angry feelings into the transference, even though she could not consciously accept the interpretations, she got in touch again with good external and internal objects, represented by the blackbird and its song. She came to life in unexpected ways, showing humour and vitality, because I think at those moments I was a robust object who could think about and withstand her anger and wit.

Mr Krol: A survivor of a concentration camp

Note how the early work with Mr Krol enabled him to begin talking about his experiences in the concentration camp. Note, too, as I heard his story unfold, the difficulties I experienced in managing my own feelings. The material is a reminder of the trauma many elderly people suffered through war experiences and provides some insight into how trauma, of whatever kind, has lasting effects into old age.

Mr Krol, a 72-year-old Polish man, was referred to me by his GP. The GP wrote that Mr Krol had a long history of anxiety and panic attacks, connected with wartime experiences in a concentration camp. Recently he had become embroiled in conflict where he lived which had made him extremely fearful. It was with some trepidation that I invited Mr Krol for an initial assessment with a view to counselling, because I had not anticipated I would be called upon to work with survivors of the concentration camps. In my *naiveté*, a defensive innocence, I had assumed that the survivors would be too old or already dead.

Mr Krol arrived punctually, a debonair man with a ready smile and a distinctive European charm. He spoke with a slight accent, but was fluent and rarely hesitated for the word he wanted. I particularly noticed his clothes because he was carefully dressed in rather lively colours, wearing a smart checked shirt with a well-matched tie. He talked at length about problems with a new flat he had recently moved to. He had become very unhappy there. Much of his distress was focused on the residents' car park which was alongside his flat. The car park was near a shopping centre and was being used by non-residents, especially young people, who disturbed him during the night as they arrived or departed. He had gone out to remonstrate with a group who then verbally abused and threatened him. He was shaken up by it. Although he was making representations to the authorities about protecting the car park, he felt pessimistic that anything would be done and regretted having moved to the flat. He felt more and more tormented by living there and had decided to try to move again, which filled him with apprehension.

Somewhat reluctantly he mentioned a bit about the rest of his life. He described a lonely, unhappy life. He had never spoken to anyone about the concentration camp and he doubted that he would be able to do so now. Nonetheless I felt he could see a connection between the torment he suffered in his new flat and the persecution in the camp. He now felt he desperately needed to talk about the concentration camp before he died. I felt this could be long and difficult work and I was glad to be able to offer him open-ended counselling. I sensed his readiness to begin and felt no need to build in a review after a few sessions. He accepted my offer of once-weekly counselling. I think he felt relieved but also frightened, and so did I.

During the following three weeks Mr Krol talked about his life before and after the war, but said little about the concentration camp. I learned he was born into a poor family, with an older sister who was his sole surviving relative and two brothers who were dead. When he was just five years old, his father, who worked in a foundry facing a hot furnace with his back exposed to the cold, died of pneumonia. He had no memories of his father, except he'd been told that when father recovered he was in for a good hiding. He described his mother as cold and strict and recalled her wanting him to sit on her lap and him running away, afraid of her. Late in her life his mother had told him that when she was in her teens she was raped. His few happy memories seemed to be of school, though he also said he played truant a great deal. He had started an apprenticeship just before the outbreak of war. Then he was incarcerated in Auschwitz because he had refused to join the German army. After two-and-a-half years he was released.

He eventually made his way to England where he had lived ever since. He had had no permanent relationships. He had fathered a son by a woman who married another man and took the boy to live abroad. He never saw his son again. From another brief relationship he had a daughter who was then raised by her mother and step-father. When his daughter got in touch with him in later years he discovered she had suffered abuse by the step-father. She lived as a single parent with a son of her own and was interested in establishing a relationship with Mr Krol. He could hardly bring himself to see her. In his forties he had a breakdown and slashed his wrists. When his wrists were being stitched the doctor told him it would hurt, but he replied that he couldn't be hurt any more. Recently Mr Krol had become involved with a widow eleven years younger. They had met in a therapy group which he had subsequently left because he couldn't talk about his experiences. He spent a lot of time with her, helped her decorate her maisonette and then, when her daughter moved out, he sometimes used to stay with her.

He described just one experience in the concentration camp. He said he had felt determined to survive and focused all his effort on acquiring food because he knew that he would perish on the rations that were provided. He recalled running to a van which was delivering some hot food. He grabbed a bundle of potatoes and hid them under his shirt. He did not notice they were hot, or realise until afterwards that they were burning his flesh.

Mr Krol remained reluctant to say more about the concentration camp. He preferred talking about his childhood and thinking about how his later difficulties might be connected with his early life. Throughout these first sessions there was a recurring theme which suggested he feared he or I would not be able to bear being exposed to his memories of the camp. For example, in the third session he spoke of feeling sorely let down after the war, having held on to the hope in the camp of one day being free and able to return to Poland, but it was then taken over by communism. Whilst acknowledging his bitterness and sadness that he had not been able to return to his country, I also talked to him about his hope for the counselling, that it would provide an opportunity to talk, and his fear that I would let him down and not be able to bear the pain of his experiences. (There were, of course, grounds for his fears because already the brief glimpse he had given me of the camp had been distressing for both of us.)

After this interpretation he recalled another occasion in the camp when he had tried to pick up a baked potato which had fallen on the ground. Three times he tried to get the potato and each time he was caught and beaten. Finally the guard crushed the potato underfoot. Mr Krol said he learned not to yell when he was beaten, because those who yelled were beaten all the more.

Four weeks later Mr Krol began telling me more about his experiences in the camp. He was just 20 when the province in which he lived was annexed by the Germans and the young men were expected to join the German army. His mother was against him joining the Germans to fight their war. The Gestapo came for him at 4.00 a.m. He remembered his mother crying and pleading with them to take her instead. After two days in a police station he was taken to Auschwitz. Conditions there were primitive, with a pump in the open for washing in summer and winter. He had to push wheelbarrows along planks and recalled having to run when the wheelbarrows were empty. They were squeezed into barracks with a German prisoner in charge. On arrival they were routinely beaten. He did not utter a sound and because of this he thought they beat him less. When he stole food, though they beat him, he wasn't reported. He told me again how he dashed to the containers of steaming potatoes and hid some under his shirt, oblivious to the burning heat, determined only to survive.

After sixteen months he was 'lucky' and got a job under shelter in a garage, spraying cars. It was an opportunity to escape but he didn't because he knew that if he did then 25 fellow prisoners would be taken as 'hostages' and killed, and he also feared the consequences for his family. But, he asked, where would he have hidden anyway? When others escaped he used to stand stiffly to attention, looking the Germans straight in the eye, because he thought that perhaps in this way they would think he was strong, a good worker, and would not take him as a hostage.

During escapes they were kept standing all night. The bodies of those whose attempts to escape were unsuccessful were displayed, and he and others had to march past and look at them. They marched to music played by bands of musicians. Later, the camp looked like a sanatorium, with decent buildings and avenues of trees. He saw the Jews arriving, mothers and children, and was told they were to take showers. The crematorium could not cope with the bodies so they were buried in mass graves.

I had to cancel the next week's session because I was ill with 'flu-like symptoms. My overriding concern was about Mr Krol because he had just started talking about the camp and I felt my absence would fulfil his worst fears. It was unusual for me to be unwell and this was the first time, since starting at the hospital nine months earlier, that I had had to cancel appointments because of illness. I phoned Mr Krol to tell him I was unwell but hoped to see him for his next appointment. I recovered and was able to see him the following week. I had been deeply shocked and upset when he told me more about the camp, but it was only later that I realised the connection between my illness and having to see him again.

He resumed his account where he had left off. Later, he admitted he felt he was not able to convey to me what it was like in the camp. He feared I would think he was making it all up, or that I would look upon what happened to him like the books or films that have been produced about the camps. It was an important moment when he realised that for much of the time in the camp he had felt detached and had looked on as though it wasn't real and he wasn't there. The reality of these experiences and the fear that he or I would become depressed and break down because of the pain, or be unaffected by it, remained issues we had to work through again and again.

Commentary

I have included some of my work with Mr Krol to illustrate how the war trauma may finally need to be brought to counselling because of the fear of dying with the trauma undigested and still persecuting. The work illustrates some of the problems of trying to digest what may ultimately be indigestible. Especially in this early work with Mr Krol, I drew heavily on supervision and my own analysis because I found the work so distressing. My supervisor's first reaction to Mr Krol was to think about the need to record his story. She didn't mean literally to tape-record it, but rather a sense she picked up that it needed to be made real, that he needed to tell his story. As she and I pieced his story together we could see how her reaction spoke of his need for his story to be heard and understood. During the first eight weeks when Mr Krol was unable to say much about the camp, I think what finally helped him to begin his story was that I was prepared simply to wait and think and talk about his anxieties and phantasies, as I understood them through my own counter-transference feelings of panic and dread.

My illness after he started talking about the concentration camp reflects my difficulty in hearing about the trauma and processing it in my mind. Because of the suddenness of my absence I explained the reason to him, unlike the planned change to the arrangements with Mrs Taylor. The week's absence didn't seem to impair the subsequent work with him. However, I had to look out for and articulate his phantasy that he had damaged me and would do so again, especially as we approached holidays when he could feel he had worn me out. My absence may have provided some reassurance that I could allow his trauma to have an impact on me and, even if it meant a temporary breakdown in containment, I could recover and return. Many months later, after a Christmas holiday, he said to me, with great feeling, referring to his reactions to the break, 'after all this, you *still* want to see me'. Throughout the work there would remain a tension for me of either losing my composure because of feeling overwhelmed with distress, or detaching myself and withdrawing from the pain.

Another aspect of Mr Krol's difficulties in talking about the camp was conveyed when he told me several times how he did not yell when the guards beat him because they would only beat him more if he did. I can now see that he was telling me about a negative transference in which he feared if he brought his distress about the camp then I would be like the guards and be cruel to him. Mr Krol was the last patient I saw in the evenings. On one occasion when I was responsible for locking the building, I was leaving in a hurry and as I sped away I was afraid I had locked Mr Krol in. I hadn't, but this experience brought home to me the power of the transference and counter-transference, of being a cruel guard.

The effects of war trauma are now classified as post-traumatic stress disorders (PTSDs). There is a considerable body of research which attests to the long-term effects of post-traumatic stress disorders associated with war trauma, often exacerbated by ageing (e.g. Robbins, 1994). A study of former Second World War prisoners of war found that 40 years later nearly one-third suffered PTSD symptoms (Speed *et al.*, 1989, quoted by Robbins). Caroline Garland has written about psycho-analytic work with patients suffering PTSD from various external disasters and suggests that the long term effects of trauma are different for each survivor because the trauma links up 'with whatever is damaged or flawed from from the survivor's past' (Garland, 1991, p. 508). In particular, because the trauma is a catastrophic assault on life and on anyone's capacity to manage anxiety, it tends to re-activate earlier problems in the nurturing relationship, including the more ordinary and inevitable flaws in any mother and infant relationship. In this way the trauma can damage an individual's subsequent capacity to process anxiety, especially the capacity to think symbolically and distinguish fantasy from reality. Consequently the trauma can be felt concretely to be the same as the original difficulties in containment. I think Mr Krol's account of the potatoes which burned his skin may illustrate this concrete thinking, in which this memory also conveys an internal state where something nourishing, a good object, has become identified with something painful and life-threatening. In other words, the trauma of the concentration camp revived (and became identified with) the early, probably ordinary, lapses in maternal care. Despite Mr Krol's account of his mother's own trauma of being raped and that she was cold to him, it is not clear that there were exceptional difficulties in his early relationship with her. She did survive the rape, just as he managed to survive the concentration camp.

In counselling Mr Krol I aimed to allow him to tell the story about the concentration camp and to have a go at digesting the trauma he was unable to process on his own. In practice the work involved in pursuing these aims is similar to the psycho-analytic psychotherapy with PTSD outlined by Garland. It meant allowing him to tell his story again and again; helping him to distinguish the reality of the evil he had endured from the internal phantasies of cruelty and destructiveness it stirred in him and in me in the counter-transference; and working through his guilt about having survived when so many perished, and his justified rage about what had happened to him. It also meant working through the earlier problems which were re-activated by the trauma of the concentration camp, and repeatedly acknowledging his feeling that he would never get over what had happened to him. My hope was that the work would enable him to feel free of some of the torment which contaminated his life, to feel less persecuted by his grievances and instead be able to feel sad about the irretrievable damage that had been done to his life. I hoped, too, he might be able to enjoy what was possible in the time that was left, even though what would be possible would fall short of what he and I wanted for him.

Postscript

Nearly four years later, as Mr Krol and I approached the end of our work together, as much to my surprise and delight as his own, he told me he was having the 'best time' in his life.

4

COUNSELLING ELDERLY COUPLES

Introduction

I have found a recent publication from the Tavistock Institute of Marital Studies extremely helpful in thinking about counselling couples. The book is called *Psychotherapy with Couples* and is a selection of papers written by staff at the Institute, edited by Stanley Ruszczynski (1993). The orientation of the book is psycho-analytic. I would like to outline some of the key ideas from the book which I have found useful. There is a general agreement amongst the authors that the marital relationship involves two ubiquitous needs: the need for intimacy and the need to be separate, with their attendant anxieties of either being swallowed up or abandoned. These anxieties resonate with our earliest experience of closeness in the infant and mother relationship. The capacity to develop and sustain a couple relationship depends on how we negotiated that first attachment in the triangular constellation known as the 'Oedipus complex'. The Oedipus complex, essentially unconscious, was first outlined by Freud and refers to the infant's and child's passionate attachment to a parent of the opposite sex and rivalry with the same sex parent. Particularly as developed by Klein, the Oedipus complex also includes a negative or inverted complex involving a passionate attachment to the same sex parent and rivalry with the opposite sex parent. Ron Britton (quoted by Fisher in this book) points out that the infant or child has to manage both being in a close relationship to mother which excludes another, especially father, and at the same time has a growing awareness of a special sexual, parental relationship from which the infant or child is excluded. Fisher describes this as 'the painfully tragic erotic attachment that reaches across a chasm, a chasm created by the inexorable difference between the generations, by the reality of the difference of the experience of being the parent and the experience of being the child' (p. 150).

In essence, working through this Oedipal dilemma means working through the anxieties of the depressive position (see Chapter 1) which arise from the realisation of feelings of love and hate for one and the same person. How well this is managed will depend on internal factors, like envy, and externally on how the parents manage the inclusion and exclusion and the kind of model of a couple which they present which can be internalised. Where there is a poor early relationship between the parents and between the parents and child, then later the marital relationship may be looked to in order to make up for what was missed and may be idealised as such. If found lacking, the marital relationship may then be denigrated because of an intolerance of any disappointment.

Working with a couple means being alert to their individual transferences to the counsellor and to one another. In so far as the couple share certain phantasies and aspects of their internal worlds, particularly their conscious and unconscious view of a marital relationship, counselling means attending to their shared transference onto the counsellor. Whether the counsellor works in a pair with another counsellor or, as in my case, works alone with a couple, it is important to keep in mind the transference onto the counsellor(s) as a couple. For example, the single counsellor's interpretations can be experienced as a product of an internal creative coupling or dialogue.

The marital transference onto the counsellor(s) is of crucial significance in this work because it offers a way of understanding the unconscious meaning of the couple's relationship. Stanley Ruszczynski describes how a partner is selected, unconsciously, as a suitable receptacle for projective identification to contain parts of oneself, *defensively* because these aspects cannot be tolerated and *with the developmental hope* that at some time it may be possible to integrate these parts within oneself; thus we establish unconscious contracts with our partner and the marital transference is a way in which these contracts may be revealed.

If all goes well the marital relationship operates as a creative container in which the tensions and conflicts between the couple can be worked through. Warren Colman writes: 'Marriage does not have to be the place where I can entirely be myself, but it can be the place where I discover some of the possibilities for becoming myself' (p. 141). Colman differentiates this notion of creative containment from 'defensive containment' in a marriage where one partner offers containment to the other as a mother does for her infant. For the elderly couple, one of the pressing tensions to be processed in the relationship is the ever encroaching reality of one's own and one's partner's death: the loss of one's own life and of a relationship. In the following stories of the couples with whom I worked, whatever the grievances and disappointments about the relationships, I think they were all struggling with the anticipation of this final abandonment.

In this chapter I use the terms 'marital relationship' and 'couples' synonymously because all the work with elderly couples reported here concerns couples who were heterosexual and married. I had no experience of working with homosexual couples: indeed, none of my elderly clients identified themselves as homosexual. I suspect this was because of the prejudices and taboos about homosexuality, which are particularly strong in this generation.

Some of the difficulties and failed attempts in counselling elderly couples

Mrs Henderson

Note the extreme splitting in this couple where it seemed Mrs Henderson had evacuated her own despair and grief into her husband and into myself in the counselling relationship. See how she remained unable to repair this split in the way she resisted her husband joining her in the sessions.

A woman in her early seventies, Mrs Henderson was referred to me by her GP because she suffered from panic attacks and claustrophobia which had only occurred in the last few years. Mrs Henderson was a quietly spoken woman and was well groomed with an air of refinement, giving the impression of a faded gentility. She spent most of the first assessment meeting complaining about her husband. Since his retirement, several years earlier, he had been angry, unpredictable and would fly into rages against her. He was furious about the retirement settlement from his job because when he retired he was given no pension, only a new car. Now their life was very restricted owing to reduced finances. Recently he had locked her in their dining room whilst she was making a weekly phone call to a friend. She felt he was jealous of her talking to her friend. Since he was at home all the time he rarely let her out of his sight. She said he often experienced a shortness of breath and was worried about dying.

Mrs Henderson mentioned that she suffered from nightmares. I asked her if she could tell me any that she remembered. She described a dream in which she got into a panic about not being able to find her way home from a particular seaside resort. I asked her about her thoughts about the dream. She said she and her husband had regularly holidayed at this resort until his retirement when they could no longer to afford to go back. They had since argued about whether they might try some cheaper form of holiday. She then described another dream in which she became very frightened because someone was trying to put a veil over her head. She had no associations to this second dream.

Towards the conclusion of this first meeting, I said I thought Mrs Henderson might also be feeling angry since her husband's retirement because of the claustrophobic existence they now lived. She too might be feeling her age and frightened of dying. Mrs Henderson looked puzzled. She said she felt the problem was her husband and his unreasonable behaviour. I said I thought it could be helpful to see her with her husband. She quickly replied he would go mad if she suggested such a thing. He would not admit he had a problem and neither would he be willing to see anybody about it. I concluded this meeting by offering her a further appointment. Again I suggested she try to talk it over with her husband and ask him to accompany her to the next appointment.

When I saw Mrs Henderson a fortnight later, she came alone and spoke in much the same way as on the first meeting, complaining about her husband's anger and the miserable life with him. She was again reluctant to consider that she shared any of her husband's feelings, and was not willing to ask him to join us in further meetings. I felt quite despairing. I said I felt the difficulties resided in the marital relationship and needed to be addressed in joint meetings, but if she changed her mind about including her husband then I would be happy to see them both in the future. Some weeks later I had a polite note from Mrs Henderson in which she thanked me for seeing her.

Commentary

Mrs Henderson is an example of a client coming for counselling but presenting someone else, in this case her husband, as the problem. In such cases it can be useful to think about whether the client is also describing problematic aspects of him- or herself and to listen to the client's account as possibly about an intra-personal difficulty, not just an interpersonal one. In other words this could be a projective process in which one member of the couple carries, and is affected by projections from the other. Projective identification often has an effect on the recipient who then believes the feelings are his or her own. So, it may be that Mr Henderson's difficult behaviour reflected a complex mixture of his own and his wife's feelings.

Mrs Henderson's dreams support an hypothesis of a projective process in which her husband was carrying unwanted feelings on her behalf. The nightmares reveal Mrs Henderson's fear of her feelings about their reduced circumstances and of her worries about dying. To interpret the dreams it was useful to think of all the material in the session as possible associations as well as to elicit specific associations from the client. Otherwise there is a danger of making erroneous interpretations based only on the counsellor's associations. Although Mrs Henderson did not produce associations for the second dream, the image of a veil being put over her head suggested some of the classical depictions of death indicated by a veil or a shroud placed over a corpse. This image resonated with her talk of her husband's fears of death. I think Mrs Henderson was too frightened to consider some of these feelings within herself and to co-operate in marital counselling in which the splitting and projection between her and her husband could be addressed. I felt, too, that Mrs Henderson evacuated some of her disappointment and frustration into me, a reason perhaps for her polite thanks.

Whilst the reduction in this couples' circumstances might have been weathered more easily earlier in their lives, it had a particularly difficult meaning at this later stage because it doubtless galvanised other losses they were experiencing, like the grief about retirement, the loss of physical capacities and the anticipation of death.

Mr and Mrs Johnson

See how I was drawn into a tormenting struggle between this couple, in which it seemed old scores about sexual jealousy were now being settled as the previously 'live wire' Mrs Johnson became incapacitated. See that in the transference I too had to experience a betrayal, especially in the way they concluded the counselling.

Mrs Johnson, a 64-year-old woman, suffered from Parkinson's Disease and had spent two weeks on the rehabilitation ward. Shortly before she was discharged she was referred by the consultant physician who was concerned about Mr Johnson being too protective of his wife. Mr Johnson complained that his wife used to hallucinate, though none of the staff on the ward had seen any evidence of it. Kay, a nurse auxiliary, was Mrs Johnson's keyworker. She felt Mrs Johnson had lost of lot of self-respect and confidence since the onset of the Parkinson's Disease, particularly because Mr Johnson now treated his wife like a child. Kay had taken her out shopping and they had bought some make-up which Mrs Johnson was now using. I asked Kay if she would be interested in joining me in some sessions with Mr and Mrs Johnson. She seemed pleased to take part, but as it happened she only attended two of the meetings, apparently because of difficulties getting away from the ward or changes in her shift.

Mrs Johnson was a slight woman, just reaching up to her husband's shoulder. She leaned on his arm as she came into the room, walking hesitantly in small steps. Her speech was sometimes difficult to understand because she spoke quickly, with all the words getting jumbled up. Sometimes her husband would act as interpreter for her speech. At times even he could not understand her and with obvious irritation he would ask her to repeat what she said.

I saw them every two weeks for one hour, over a period of five months. Each time they came, Mr Johnson would begin by complaining about his wife's hallucinations. Mrs Johnson would listen impassively as though her husband was talking about someone else. On one occasion I met Mr and Mrs Johnson's son visiting on the ward and he confirmed that his mother did hallucinate, mostly seeing himself and his brother when they were small. However, Mrs Johnson's husband said she also used to say another man was poking her on the sofa, or she would accuse Mr Johnson of being unfaithful. The hallucinations made Mr Johnson extremely angry and he would appeal to me to rid his wife of them. I thought the hallucinations were a distraction from the grief about Mrs Johnson's illness and increasing disability, but I felt under pressure to make sense of the content of the hallucinations.

As the history of Mrs Johnson's illness emerged, it was clear it had dealt a dreadful blow to their plans for retirement. Mr Johnson had had to retire several months early in order to take care of his wife. They had planned to move to a bungalow by the sea but now felt this was impossible because of Mrs Johnson's condition. During the time I saw them she began to experience increasing difficulty climbing the stairs at home. More and more Mr Johnson felt she could not be left alone. When his wife had become ill, Mr Johnson's three brothers all died within a short space of time. I felt he was still shocked and grieving these deaths and his wife's illness. Although he looked tearful when I said this, he could not admit to feeling sad and instead he started to talk again about his wife's hallucinations.

It seemed Mr and Mrs Johnson's marital relationship had probably been an unhappy one for some time before her illness. On one occasion, with some bitterness in his voice, Mr Johnson described his wife as always being aloof and inaccessible, just like I thought she often appeared in the sessions. They were quite isolated with few friends, one son lived abroad whom they rarely saw and another, though living nearby, only seemed to visit infrequently. I had the impression that they had lived a lonely life for some time, though Mr Johnson complained that they were isolated because his wife refused to go out for fear of people seeing her in a disabled state.

From the beginning I was aware of a sexual theme in the material about making Mrs Johnson more attractive with make-up and the hallucinations about a man poking her, or her accusations that her husband was unfaithful. When I took up this theme they admitted their sexual relationship had ceased some years before. Mrs Johnson looked hurt as we discussed sex and she implied that she felt sex had stopped for no good reason. Mr Johnson was clearly embarrassed. He talked about how awkward he felt about becoming a nurse for his wife and looking after her in such intimate ways as bathing her and assisting her in the toilet. They were unused to such physical intimacy and would never previously have even entered the bathroom together.

Several weeks after I started seeing them, they went out to a social club, the first time for many months. They were clearly pleased to tell me about this excursion, but then Mr Johnson described in great detail the embarrassment about taking his wife to the toilet during the evening. I wondered why he had made such a business of it, asking the other women present not to use the toilet whilst he was in there with his wife. I thought he could have asked another woman to take his wife. I felt the evening had probably been painful because it would have reminded them of earlier times they had enjoyed together before Mrs Johnson became ill. They would have been confronted with how disabled she had become, no longer the 'live wire' dancer she once was. But instead of this pain they became embroiled in an argument about Mr Johnson taking her to the toilet.

The hallucinations remained a recurring issue, which I began to find irritating. It seemed the hallucinations might have been a side-effect of the medication for the treatment of the Parkison's Disease. Some alterations had been made in the medication with little noticeable effect. However, Mr Johnson persisted in questioning me about the possible biochemical origin of these symptoms. I admitted the uncertainty, but would remind him that the medics had referred his wife because they were puzzled. Moreover, it was probably a complex interaction between the physical and emotional consequences of the illness. I spoke about noticing that whenever Mrs Johnson or her husband began expressing some of their sad feelings, the other one would start talking about the hallucinations. When it seemed there was some evidence that Mrs Johnson's Parkinsons Disease was worsening, they again became preoccupied with the hallucinations.

On three occasions during the time I saw them, they consulted doctors about the hallucinations, each time without warning me. On the second and third occasion they were seen by a member of the psycho-geriatric team. I felt they came back after the consultations in a triumphant attitude, telling me they had been reassured the hallucinations were biochemical in origin. On the final occasion they said they would prefer to continue seeing the doctor who had given them such helpful advice. I agreed that it would be confusing to continue seeing myself and the doctor at the same time, but said if they wanted to pursue counselling I would see them again. They did not return.

Commentary

Counselling Mr and Mrs Johnson was hindered by a strong negative transference including envy and jealousy which I think I failed to address sufficiently. To some extent I became disabled and unable to think about their envious attacks on myself who was able-bodied, relatively young and employed. It would have been useful to talk to Mr and Mrs Johnson about how they experienced me (in the transference) as a disabled counsellor who was hallucinating useless interpretations about their inner worlds in contrast to the helpful doctors who gave them physical explanations and reassurance. The negative transference was especially important because it seemed to reflect a disparaged view of their marriage, a view which probably had a long history and which was exacerbated by Mrs Johnson's illness. The sexual jealousy and envy which emerged in the sessions seemed to hook into a lifetime's quarrel with each other. Their individual transferences to each other were also enacted in the counselling with me: Mr Johnson took over so many of his wife's jobs making her retired like he had been and eventually retiring me off; Mrs Johnson tormented her husband with the hallucinations so that he thought he might lose his mind, just as she feared she might become a 'cabbage'; and I too began to find the hallucinations tormenting, interfering with my capacity to think about what was going on. They also passed onto me a sense of betrayal in the way they consulted the doctors without warning, probably the feeling of how they felt their expectations for retirement had been betrayed as well as how they perhaps felt betrayed during their marriage. The hostility expressed in the negative transference enabled this couple to avoid the excruciating pain of their predicament: how to maintain their adult and sexual relationship when, because of a debilitating illness, their relationship had been reduced to one like that of a mother and helpless infant. It may be that some of my difficulty in working with this couple and perhaps Kay's, the nurse auxiliary who left the sessions, reflected a wish to avoid fully confronting their pain.

Some open-ended counselling of a couple: Mr and Mrs Day

The Assessment Sessions

Despite Mr Day's passivity during the assessment, note that he co-operated in providing an informative account of his history and brought some unconscious material in a dream. See how his response to the interpretation of the dream augured well for the counselling.

Mr Day, a man in his early seventies, was referred by his GP who was worried Mr Day was suffering with depression. A once active man, he had become more and more passive, spending most of the day sitting in an armchair at home. At first I saw Mr Day for three one-hour meetings each fortnight. He reminded me of an archetypal major general, an upright solid man, with a ruddy complexion and a silver grey moustache. When I asked him about himself he immediately talked about some of his experiences in the Second World War. It seemed he had had something of a breakdown whilst fighting in the trenches. He experienced a mental blackout when asked to perform a routine duty and could not explain what had happened to him. He was promptly sent off to see a doctor in a nearby village. As he arrived at the village he noticed the local padre's house and thought he could either go to the doctor or the padre. Instead he decided to simply go back to his platoon where no further enquiries were made about what had happened to him. He continued his career in the army without a recurrence of this troubling episode.

Mr Day was quite a raconteur and seemed to enjoy entertaining me with stories of his war exploits, including an especially frightening period when he had to clear land mines. Just prior to his blackout he had received news that his fiancée had broken off their engagement. He felt devastated, but soon after started regular correspondence with a boyhood friend's sister with whom he had kept in touch. At the conclusion of the war when he came home he proposed and they soon married, despite some opposition from her family who feared he might be marrying on the rebound.

Mr Day told me about his early life. His parents had both worked 'in service' as servants in a large house. Then his father, whom he described as gentle, had made a career as a stationmaster. His mother was in poor health during his childhood and died some years before his father. He had a memory of being told his father dreamed he was hitting a rat, only to wake up and find that he was hitting his wife who was in bed beside him. Mr Day was fond of both his parents. He was very close to his only sister, who was a few years his senior and who had died several years earlier of Parkinson's Disease. He said he had had a happy childhood and marriage.

After the war he had pursued training and qualified in a profession. He said he always tended to see the more negative side of things, feeling he was a pessimist. In the last few years he had become lazy, 'opting out', feeling he didn't want to do anything and not knowing why. He did little around the house and had lost interest in activities which previously he enjoyed. For example, he had a talent for drawing and liked doing watercolours and making Christmas cards for his friends, but he had stopped all the art work. He said his wife wore the pants, she was full of energy and she was in the driving seat, quite literally because she used to drive him to these appointments. Five or six years ago, during a holiday, his wife had said she was disappointed in him and no longer loved him. At about that time they had ceased having a sexual relationship. He said he realised he'd always had to take the initiative and that she didn't really enjoy sex. In mid-life he had had some psychiatric treatment when he had been prescribed tranquillisers which he had gradually 'weaned' himself off.

In the third meeting, Mr Day brought a dream in which he was travelling on the underground and did not know in which direction to go, and didn't have anyone to talk to about it either. His association to the dream was the story about the choice between the padre and the doctor after his blackout, when he had chosen neither. I said I thought the dream was about the choice now before him, whether to pursue some counselling with me; and his anxiety that again he would not choose to do so, that he'd have no one to talk to, when perhaps it now felt more urgent to sort things out at the end of his life before he died. Mr Day said he wasn't conscious of this, but he looked interested in the interpretation. At the conclusion of this meeting I said I felt it would be better for me to see Mr Day and his wife together and, provided she agreed, for us to meet once a fortnight for an hour, on an open-ended basis. Mr Day was pleased to include his wife and agreed to bring her to the next meeting.

Commentary

Mr Day presents a complementary example to Mrs Henderson (see Chapter 4) of someone willingly identifying himself as the problem in contrast to his wife, whereas Mrs Henderson only saw the problems in her husband. It was because of this polarised view of himself and his wife that I suspected Mr Day might be incapacitated by a projective process in the marital relationship. So I decided to extend the assessment over three sessions to give me time to think about whether to include his wife in the sessions. I came to the view that there was a splitting process in this marital relationship in which all the interest and liveliness resided in Mrs Day, whilst Mr Day had become inert and depressed. I hypothesised that Mr Day may have been carrying some of his wife's depression, just as she was now a receptacle for his capacities. In order to address this split I thought it would be more expedient to work with them both.

Supervision helped me to see the anger expressed in Mr Day's passivity, an anger perhaps with a wife who was felt to be second best and whom he hurt by giving her the pants to wear. Though he looked the part of a major general, he may have felt ill-prepared by his gentle father for asserting himself and being openly aggressive.

An encouraging sign for psychodynamic work was Mr Day bringing a dream to the third meeting, which felt like a gift of some unconscious material. Despite his passivity, unconsciously there was a part of him which was actively co-operating in the counselling. The dream indicated his deep ambivalence about exploring the 'underground' of his unconscious. In the context of being an elderly client, the reference in Mr Day's associations to the padre made me think of his conscious and unconscious awareness of death and therefore a greater sense of urgency to get on with counselling now. His response to my interpretation of the dream was further confirmation of his readiness for counselling: he made a distinction between what was conscious and unconscious and he seemed interested in learning more about the unconscious.

First sessions with Mr and Mrs Day

Note how during these early sessions I seemed to be seduced by this couple into feeling hopeful, only to be disappointed when they kept reporting that the counselling made no difference. Like Penelope of the Greek legends, they seemed to unpick the work between the sessions, but note how difficult I found it to confront them about this process.

Mrs Day joined her husband in the sessions after a Chistmas break. She impressed me as a forceful woman. She wore no make-up, had her grey hair simply cut and swept back and wore somewhat plain clothes. She nonetheless exuded an unmistakable sensuality, which puzzled me in the light of her husband's complaints about her disinterest in sex. She soon launched into a tirade of complaints about Mr Day whom she described as a 'vegetable', wanting her to do practically everything. Things had been 'all right' with her husband until about five years ago, though he had been very dependent on her for a long time. Her life revolved around the two dogs, one their own and the other an older dog which belonged to her 90-year-old mother who had been living with them for several years. Mrs Day took the dogs for long walks each day and she felt very resentful that her husband had gradually stopped accompanying her. He looked on rather meekly during this angry speech and merely said the walks were now too much for him. Her riposte was that the less he exercised the more disabled he would become. She was obviously irritated by his concerns about his physical state and impatient that he would not extend himself, even if it did mean some discomfort. With some sadness she said she felt lonely and missed his company on the walks. She said he spent most of the time slumped in a chair and they hardly talked to one another any more. She felt their marriage was no longer a partnership. Mr Day then spoke about the time she said she didn't love him any more and his hurt about that. Toward the end of this meeting Mrs Day said she felt hopeless and asked me 'Where does this all lead?' I felt somewhat thrown because I was impressed with how open they had both been, and it seemed to me that they had started talking.

Over the next sessions a pattern emerged in which Mrs Day would arrive looking pained and produce numerous complaints about her husband since the previous meeting. Mr Day usually had little to say in his defence but would look embarrassed and hurt. I often felt drawn into siding with Mrs Day against her husband, trying to urge him into life. At the same time I tried to resist this because I could see it made him withdraw into passivity.

I learned that Mrs Day's mother was French and her father was about 30 years older than her mother. Her mother sounded a forbidding figure. Mrs Day recalled an incident from her childhood in which her mother slammed the lid of the piano on her fingers as she was playing it. She said her mother insisted the children always went early to bed before her father came home, so, fond as she was of him, she saw little of him. Mrs Day did not feel close to her mother, whom she described as a cold woman. As an adult Mrs Day had been hurt by her mother's criticism. Since Mrs Day's mother came to live with them Mr and Mrs Day organised their life around her: for example, rarely going out at lunch time because the mother liked to have a cooked lunch prepared for her. They had taken the mother to live with them in their small bungalow when she had no longer been able to look after herself. There was now little room for either of them to pursue former hobbies and interests at home.

Mrs Day's mother tended to sit most of the day like Mr Day. She rarely spoke except to give monosyllabic replies to questions. Mrs Day excused her mother's silence as due to having spent the latter part of her life on her own. Curiously, Mrs Day, like her husband, described a childhood memory which included a rat. She talked about a time when as a young girl she looked into a small outhouse for a door key and screamed because she saw the red eyes of a rat staring at her.

For some years after they were married, Mr and Mrs Day tried to conceive without success, so they adopted a baby boy. Two years after the adoption Mrs Day gave birth to a son. During their adolescence both sons were somewhat estranged from the parents who seemed to experience a lot of guilt about them. It seemed they felt closer to their natural son who was married with children, whereas they described their adopted son as cold, aloof and divorced from an unhappy marriage.

Mrs Day knew about her husband's failed engagement. She was, I think, rather irritated that Mr Day had, throughout their marriage, kept in touch with his former fiancée. Mr Day spoke of feeling inferior to his wife, who came from a well-to-do family unlike his own. He spoke of her lack of interest in sex. She said angrily that he had left her alone for so long she was not prepared to have a physical relationship with him now.

Commentary

The start of the work with the Days shows the problems when there is a strong positive counter-transference. I was disappointed each time this couple came back complaining after I felt we had done some good work in the previous session. But I was unable to think about the attacks in these complaints on me and the work. I so liked them I found it difficult to think of their aggressiveness, perhaps reflecting a rather idealised transference of mine onto them as elderly parents I could enjoy.

Supervision enabled me to eventually take up the attacks (see Post script below) I became more aware of how I sometimes joined with Mrs Day in criticising her husband, just as they sometimes ganged up with each other against me. I saw the effects on this elderly couple of having an even older parent living with them: they were reduced to a childlike state, living as brother and sister in the presence of a tyrannical mother; and in his passivity Mr Day seemed to be in competition with his mother-in-law for his wife's attentions.

Following an Easter holiday

Note that after this first holiday in the counselling, the negative transference was expressed in a concerted attack on myself who seemed to represent a potent sexual couple. At the same time, see how they continued to provoke each other, in Mrs Day's relentless criticisms of her husband and in his retaliatory passivity, with the result that they could not engage with each other in a satisfying or creative way.

When they resumed the sessions Mr Day began by saying they weren't getting anywhere. He said the sessions were simply opening up old wounds which were hurtful, they were not uplifting and he was not feeling any better. Mrs Day said little, though she looked frustrated and appeared to agree the sessions were useless. She complained again about feeling a prisoner and having to look after her husband and her mother. Mr Day then described a time when he felt very angry with his wife. He was doing some decorating, painting a ceiling in extremely hot weather. After he had finished his wife came in and instead of any praise for his efforts she pointed out some paint which had dropped on the carpet. He was furious and had not done any painting since. At the conclusion of this session, as they were about to leave, Mr Day turned to his wife and asked her if it was convenient for them to come to the session next week. I felt really put in my place!

When they returned the next fortnight, Mrs Day began by talking about a television programme they'd started watching which had some explicit sex in it. They turned it off in disgust. I made a link with how they had turned away from their own sexual relationship. Mrs Day seemed genuinely puzzled about what had gone wrong between them because they had had such an enjoyable sexual relationship, almost 'too good'. I wondered aloud whether it felt 'too good to last': if their relationship was too good then the anticipation of the end of their lives together would be too painful, so it might feel preferable to end on a sour note. Later, there was some talk about the shadow of the other woman, like a paint stain on their relationship.

The following fortnight there was a long discussion about how they had apportioned the different domestic jobs since Mr Day retired. Mrs Day seemed annoyed that Mr Day wanted to do the washing up and vacuuming and make the beds, jobs she felt were for women. Mr Day felt it was the least he could do and he rather liked doing those jobs. I felt some sympathy for Mrs Day's view that her husband wanted to take over the woman's jobs and would not do the manly work around the house. Later in supervision I could see that there was also a dispute about the nice jobs and who would do them. Mrs Day seemed to want to keep all the nice jobs to herself.

They came to the next session looking a good deal happier and even shared a joke together. They laughed about a repair man who was working in the house during their lunch hour. He misunderstood Mr Day's question to him about whether he had had lunch as an invitation to lunch with them. They were relieved he did not accept. Then they talked about having to keep the two dogs apart when the male dog got 'randy'. When I picked up the sexual theme, Mrs Day railed against her mother for making hurtful accusations about her being promiscuous when she was an adolescent and generally for being a critical presence in their household. Mr Day spoke of going to art lessons after he retired and then dropping out after the teacher was critical of him. They both recalled enjoying going bowling together and then stopping for no obvious reason.

At the next session Mr Day talked at length about his career, relishing the memories in stories of his work. He said there were various changes now with the introduction of computers and other new techniques. Sadly he admitted he wouldn't be able to do the work any more even if he were allowed back. Then they both began to argue about his reluctance to do anything now. He said activities like gardening caused him too much physical discomfort. His wife objected that by doing less and less he would become even more unfit. I found myself feeling irritated with him and asked why was it so important not to feel any discomfort? Again Mrs Day was particularly unhappy that he no longer joined her on the walks with the dogs. She said she couldn't share the pleasures of the walks with him. He was cross and said she didn't talk to him when she was at home. I said I felt this argument about the walks illustrated the resentment which was being passed back and forth between them.

Commentary

In retrospect I can see a strong negative transference to me following the Easter holiday. The complaints about lack of any progress were especially virulent and for both of them I had become a critical presence drawing attention to the stains in their relationship, like the paint dropped on the carpet. Unconsciously, I think they were both laughing at me, like the repair man, for my thinking that they wanted my company. They joined together in making attacks on me who, in the transference represented a potent sexual couple, treating me as a 'randy dog' who had to be separated from its mate. With my relative youth, my holiday and having a job to return to after it, it was as though I was flaunting my potency in front of them. It would have been helpful if I could have interpreted these unconscious negative feelings towards me and shown the couple how these feelings were used to avoid sad feelings about loss evoked by my absence during the holiday. I think I felt somewhat frightened of challenging the denial of depending on me because of a fear of their dependency which can be a particular problem for a younger therapist working with elderly clients (Martindale, 1989a). When Mr Day did bring some of his sad feelings about the loss of his work, they quickly became embroiled in bickering. I tended to be drawn into the argument, joining in an avoidance of their pain of the sadness about the losses in their lives so far and about the losses which lay ahead.

The material in these sessions reveals the effects of the Days' own early experience of their parents' marriages on their marital relationship. They shared an intolerance of any failings in the relationship, like the paint stain on the carpet. Mrs Day couldn't seem to bear the stain without criticising Mr Day and he couldn't bear the criticism. The marital relationship was meant to make up for their poor experiences of their parents' marriages. At the same time they did not know what to do with a potent couple whether represented by the dogs or myself, or themselves when they were first married trying to conceive, because neither of them had much of an experience of a happy parental couple.

Approaching the summer holiday

Note how the preceding work on Mr and Mrs Day's resentment subsequently released some positive feelings for each other and towards me in the transference. Note, in contrast to previous sessions, how the anticipation of loss revived by the next holiday is approached in a less persecutory way and with more of a sense of sadness.

The next session, which I shall report in more detail, took place a month before the summer holiday. Mr and Mrs Day came back in a happier mood. They reported Mr Day had been walking a bit with his wife, they had enjoyed some outings together at their church and with their son, his wife and their grandchildren. When I asked which son they were talking about, Mrs Day said their natural son, and she added that their adopted son who was divorced had no children. Rather wistfully, she wondered whether, if he had had some children, the children might have kept him and his wife together. She also said how it was better to have someone to look after, like her mother, because it helped her put up with her husband. I said I wondered if she didn't have her mother to look after, would she put up with her husband? She laughed and said that thought had occurred to her. I said perhaps Mr Day was exploiting this situation because he knew his wife wouldn't leave so long as she had to look after her mother? Mr Day replied rather sourly: 'Not consciously'.

Then Mr Day described two dreams he had had since the previous meeting. In the first dream he was in a large void, a space like an aircraft hangar, with a lot of men who all looked alike. They were having stew, but there was no cutlery to eat it with. The second dream was about a 'well constructed' Victorian house which had a basement flat going underground. Mr Day was checking the flat, the plumbing, and so on with a team of men. The dream then changed to a picture of a large building with many small cubicles which he felt were for children and he felt very upset. He woke up and asked his wife what time it was, something he rarely did.

The hangar reminded him of one used by the navy. All the men looked like Mr Thorpe, a man he had met on the walks with his wife. Mr Thorpe's wife was presently in hospital with knee trouble and the Days had wondered how Mr Thorpe would manage without her. Mr Day said he liked walking with Mr and Mrs Thorpe because they walked slowly and he could keep up with them, whereas Mrs Day strode ahead. Mrs Day then complained about having to look after her mother as no one else was able to do so. She was angry that she had recently strained herself doing the gardening which she had to do all by herself because her husband would not help her. It was not a partnership any more.

I asked about the second dream. Mr Day had no associations to it, but Mrs Day said there had been accounts in the papers recently of children being locked up in a room by their parents and shut away from their friends: awful stories. Mr Day objected that he wasn't aware of having read anything like that.

I said the first dream reminded me that Mrs Day had recently had to go into hospital (for a minor operation). Mr Day quickly added that he too had been into hospital for a prostate operation which was successful and now his medication had been reduced. I said I thought the dream was about Mr Day's thoughts about death, about who will die first and a worry that like Mr Thorpe he would be left alone. Mrs Day quickly agreed, saying that she noticed in the dream there was no one to serve him the food and nothing to eat it with. She then talked about her husband's breakdown some years before when he used to follow her everywhere, even waiting outside the toilet until she came out. He used to get very worried whenever she left him. Mr Day said he still tended to feel this way. He recalled waiting with his mother-in-law for his wife to return and getting rather upset because she was late. He said to his mother-in-law, 'Come on, let's put the kettle on', as though that would magically make his wife arrive. On another occasion when he was out walking with his wife and the light was beginning to fade, he temporarily lost sight of her and then anxiously thought something had happened to her. He felt angry when she finally came back.

I then linked the second dream with the earlier interpretation, seeing it as an elaboration of the anxieties in the first one. I said that it showed the child-like feelings of being helpless and alone, stirred in the fading light at the end of his life. Another aspect that occurred to me was that so long as Mr Day could remain in a helpless and dependent state on his wife then he could feel that she would never die and leave him. But if he began to be more active then his fear was he might lose her. Reciprocally Mrs Day could feel that so long as she was needed by her husband and mother she could never die. In other words they had reached an unconscious agreement by which they could defy death.

At the end of this session Mr Day asked me what he should do and whether making these things conscious would help him change? I said I thought he was wanting some reassurance from me and was turning to me in a helpless and dependent way. I said it was painful to face the uncertainty of who will die first and who will be left alone. I acknowledged that they were bringing these worries in order to understand more and with the hope that they could change. I finished the session by telling them of the dates for my holiday in a month's time.

In the next session they returned again with reports of no improvement. I felt particularly disappointed because I thought we had done some good work on the dreams and had looked forward to seeing them again. They talked about the burden of having Mrs Day's mother living with them. I wondered if they were also burdened with a sense of guilt about waiting for her to die and a secret wish that she would die. In the final session before the holiday Mr Day said he had 'thrown a wobbly' a few days before. Whilst out on his own he suddenly felt he was going to faint or pass out. I talked about the fear of death we had seen in the dreams. To my surprise, Mrs Day admitted she sometimes was afraid of having a stroke when she was out walking alone. Apparently her father had several strokes and she feared the same thing might happen to her. She also talked rather sadly about missing her husband on her walks and not being able to share them with him. Mr Day, sorrowfully said how close they had once been. They used to go to art exhibitions and instinctively knew which works of art the other liked.

I linked Mr Day's 'wobbly' with worries stirred by the holiday and the losses in their lives they were grieving, including the anticipation of their deaths. Mr Day rather querously asked me how, if he decided to go out again on his own, would he know he wouldn't throw another wobbly? I said I thought if he became more alive in himself and to their former good relationship, then he would have to face the pain that life was coming to an end, whereas if the relationship was awful then he would have no regrets about dying. At the end of the session he turned to me and said 'When did the rot set in?' I said the rot seemed a reference to awareness of ageing, physical decline and mortality.

Commentary

This session shows a breakthrough in the counselling. It was the first one, during six months work, in which the Days acknowledged any sense of improvement. I think the turning point was when in the previous session I got hold of the resentment which they expressed to each other. Months later, in several sessions they returned to the theme of resentment and how much their new awareness of it helped them free themselves of its spoiling effects. My supervisor pointed out that whenever the resentment was acknowledged, Mr Day came out of his inert state, regained his capacity to think and was able to contribute helpful thoughts in the sessions. Only much later was I able to take up their resentment of me in the transference.

The dreams again felt like a gift from the unconscious, confirming their appreciative feelings. In arriving at an interpretation of the dreams, the preamble about their adoptive son's marriage which might have been saved by children and about Mrs Day's looking after her mother keeping her with her husband, seemed relevant associative material. It was useful, too, to have Mrs Day's associations because it made the dreams more clearly a shared piece of material which I was gradually able to interpret in terms of their relationship. I think my gaucherie in making a shift from interpreting the dream from Mr Day's perspective to thinking about what it revealed about the relationship reflects my difficulty in moving from working individually, where I would focus on the transference meaning of the dream and be primarily concerned about the individual's internal world, to working with a couple, where (as

Warren Colman writes) the focus is 'on the interaction between the couple *as an end in itself* (Colman, 1993, p. 73). I take this focus to include the couple's shared transferences about the marital relationship and also, where it seems relevant, their individual transferences to one another and to the counsellor(s).

The unconscious contract to defy death, revealed in the dreams, may also explain some of the Days' resistance to the counselling in their unpicking of the work between the sessions. Evelyn Cleavely writes that change may be resisted because it could seem to threaten life itself, so the couple may unconsciously agree to keep hope alive 'but forever around the corner' (1993, p. 67).

The success of the interpretation about the dreams can be seen in the emergence of new material when Mr and Mrs Day talked about fears of each other dying as well as their own fears of death, something I was astonished to hear from Mrs Day who seemed to take pride in her youthfulness and vigour. Some of the anxieties, especially the infantile fears of being abandoned, were doubtless provoked by the approach of my summer holiday. But I think the infantile fears were intensified by this elderly couple's awareness of the 'rot' of physical decline. I felt they approached these worries with more tolerance for sad feelings as a result of the work we had been able to do.

Postscript

I continued working with the Days for many more months. They returned from the summer holiday with the same complaints as previously. I had some more time available and I decided to offer them weekly sessions because I felt the gap between the fortnightly sessions was too long. We still struggled with a great deal of negativity which was largely expressed in their grievances that nothing was changing between them. I had been struck by the references they both made to rats in the accounts of their early lives, which I think resonated with something quite cruel going on between them and between them and me. I was eventually able to take up their spoiling attacks in a session before Christmas when they protested about some young kids who had been killing birds with peashooters. I talked about the kids in the room who were shooting at me and our work, killing off any hope. Mr Day said he felt things went bad between them twenty years earlier when their boys left home and they were thrown back on themselves. The weekly complaints lessened. Evidence of further change came after Christmas when the Days returned with a plan for a holiday for themselves later in the year. Mrs Day had found a local authority home where her mother could stay which would enable them to have a holiday on their own, something they had not done for a very long time.

Mr and Mrs Day had another successful holiday. But as the counselling came to an end they became entrenched again in mutual hostility and denigration of the counselling. So, when the counselling finished I was left in a very uncomfortable position of not knowing whether the gains that had been achieved would survive.

5

Counselling an Elderly Man Who Could Not Talk

Introduction

Valerie Sinason has written of long-term psychotherapy with a severely handicapped young woman called Maureen who had no speech (Sinason, 1992). It is a marvellous piece which inspired me to undertake the work reported in this chapter. Sinason described her work with Maureen as 'finding meaning without words' and explained that 'It is precisely the weight of meaning behind every gesture that we can find unbearable' (1992, p. 223). She draws attention to a particular method in working with patients with no speech, little symbolic play or other means of communication: 'It means working far more with the counter-transference feelings and checking them out by the response of the patient. These intuitive responses are clearly honed and deepened by training, [personal] analysis and supervision' (p. 251).

It may be recalled that counter-transference refers to all the feelings which are evoked in the counsellor by opening himself to the emotional impact of the client (see Chapter 1). The client projects feelings, often of an unbearable nature, into the counsellor with the hope that the feelings can be understood and made bearable for the client: a process which Bion described as containment, beginning in the mother-infant relationship (see Chapter 1 on projective identification). The underlying mechanism is described as projective identification because the recipient of the projections, in this case the counsellor, identifies with the projections and experiences the feelings as his own. Contemporary work about counter-transference recognises how acutely perceptive clients are about therapists' or counsellors' states of mind, and consequently clients can accurately project into the counsellor's feelings: for example, into the counsellor's wish to be a good mother to the client or into the counsellor's sadism (Brenman Pick, 1988; Young, 1995). As a result of training, personal therapy and supervision, the counsellor disentangles personal feelings and transference reactions from feelings which the client is communicating unconsciously. Sinason has demonstrated how using the counter-transference can help severely handicapped patients feel known and understood. For example, she was able to understand the different emotional meanings that a patient's head-banging expressed at different occasions. My aim was to try to understand and communicate with an elderly man who could not speak, by thinking and talking about the impact he had on me.

My first encounter with Mr Mitchell was just a few months after my arrival at the hospital. He was a patient in long-stay care and referred to me by the ward's consultant physician because of 'behaviour problems'. I met the ward sister and some of her staff to discuss the referral. They told me Mr Mitchell was an 80-year-old man who had suffered two strokes. After his first stroke, a few years earlier, he had returned home. They thought he had been looked after by a neighbour or family friends. His wife had died some years previously. When he had a second stroke he lost his speech and the right side of his body was paralysed. He could no longer be managed at home. He had been an in-patient in the hospital for just a few months before he was referred to me. He had two sons, though only one of them visited at all regularly. There seemed to be some ill feeling between the sons and between the son who didn't visit and Mr Mitchell. Sometimes the son who visited weekly brought his two children. Mr Mitchell was obviously delighted to see his grandchildren. There were also occasional visits from the woman friend or neighbour who had looked after him. She told the staff Mr Mitchell had been very kind to her. He had been a bricklayer of exceptional skill. Little more was known about his life.

Mr Mitchell was unable to speak except to shout obscenities. Still very strong physically, he would occasionally hit out at the staff when they were attending to him. He sometimes shouted throughout the day and into the night, causing an uproar on the ward as other patients shouted back. There were mixed views about whether Mr Mitchell could understand what was said to him. Sometimes he appeared to understand and sometimes not. The staff said occasionally he answered 'yes' when they felt he meant 'no', and sometimes 'no' when he meant 'yes'. He was known to be illiterate. The staff appealed to me for help about the shouting and hitting out. A young female nurse who was Mr Mitchell's keyworker was particularly upset. She felt guilty about not wanting to work with Mr Mitchell because he could be so abusive and difficult. She said she did not look forward to seeing him and was aware of leaving him to the end of her list.

I decided to try to work jointly with Mr Mitchell and his keyworker. I arranged a meeting with them both but the keyworker was unavailable, so I saw Mr Mitchell with the ward sister. I had some coloured felt tip pens and paper available in case he might be able to draw something or make some marks to communicate with me. Sister brought him to my office. He was a tall, well-built man, towering over his wheelchair. He was almost bald and had no teeth, which sometimes gave his face a babyish look. He had a fine aquiline profile and he also reminded me of a venerable ancient Roman. I drew up a chair near him and said I'd like to know a bit about him. I asked him when he was born. He turned to the sister, laughed and then sobbed inconsolably for most of that time with me. I felt profoundly shocked.

Over the next few months I met with the keyworker alone because I felt reluctant to see Mr Mitchell again. I thought there was little I could achieve because of the difficulties in communicating with him, but essentially I think I was frightened of the pain of his distress. During the time I saw his keyworker I became worried that Mr Mitchell was being physically abused by some of the staff and I describe the work about this towards the end of Chapter 8. I saw Mr Mitchell again some months later when he was present at some of the patient and staff meetings I conducted for his ward (see Chapter 11 for a description of the meetings). At times he shouted expletives throughout these meetings, so I had some first-hand experience of what the staff complained about.

Fifteen months after my first meeting with Mr Mitchell the staff again asked me for help with him. By then I felt more able to face the pain and offered to see him once a week, arranging to see him for half hourly sessions in the early evening. I saw him for a total of twenty-nine sessions over the next eight months until he died. I shall now report some of the work as it developed over that time.

Working with Mr Mitchell

Note that, despite Mr Mitchell's incapacity to speak, there developed some language between us through my searching for meaning in his behaviour and through thinking about my counter-transference. But note the difficulty in facing some of the feelings stirred in me by this work and particularly of staying with Mr Mitchell's sad feelings. Finally, note the difficulty of finding a way of being with Mr Mitchell when he was dying.

I established a routine of going to the ward to collect Mr Mitchell and taking him to my office. When I first went to him I would tell him who I was, where we were going and why. I said the staff were worried about his unhappiness and we hoped that the meetings with me might help. In my office, which was a short distance from his ward, I positioned his wheelchair alongside and at an angle from where I sat. I did not put the wheelchair brakes on but left them free.

Very soon in the first session, using his left, unparalysed arm, he wheeled himself away from me until he reached the wall. He began shouting angrily. He had a loud and piercing voice which I found quite frightening. Occasionally he put the brake on the left wheel and then tried to move the wheel, which of course would not budge. Sometimes he groaned and for brief periods he was quiet.

My fear was that I would be as speechless as Mr Mitchell. To my relief I found I had some thoughts and was able to share them with him. I talked about how stuck and helpless he felt, perhaps frightened of his rage and consumed with grief. I wondered, too, if he felt he had put a brake on his life, as though he was responsible for the stroke. After I spoke he sometimes looked at me, as if to ask me what it was I had said. I felt unsure whether he had understood anything I was saying.

I took the session to supervision. My supervisor helped me think about how frightened Mr Mitchell was of me and what I might do to him because it seemed to her he was probably cowering in fear against the wall. She suggested to me that Mr Mitchell's stroke probably felt like a clamp on him or a straitjacket, and he was locked inside a damaged body, though he was letting me know there was something inside him that he could manoeuvre like the wheelchair. She encouraged me to explain more of the purpose of the counselling to him, remind him of the length of the sessions and that I would be taking him back to the ward. She suggested I look out for any signs from him that he felt what I said was right or wrong.

At the third session he seemed more friendly as I arrived to collect him. In my room he stayed longer with me before he backed away to the wall. But this time he gave out a terrible wail, over and over again, like a child crying for a lost or broken toy. Interspersed with his cries he shouted angrily again. Sometimes in his cries it was as if he was also calling out 'Hallo there', as though trying to reach out. Then he seemed very frustrated when he couldn't get through to me. However, there were two or three times when he seemed to agree with what I said. For a short while it felt like the flow of an ordinary conversation. For example, I found myself feeling fed up and when I said I thought he probably felt fed up, he looked interested and seemed to say 'yeh'.

Taking this session to supervision helped me understand more of Mr Mitchell's unrelieved misery: that it was so bad nothing could make it better, and though he was hoping for some release he was probably also frightened of death which might come with another stroke.

Arriving at the ward for the fourth session I learned that Mr Mitchell's son had been expected but hadn't turned up. Once in my room Mr Mitchell pulled his chair away to the wall and didn't move back throughout the session. I felt there were only one or two moments of contact between us in the whole time. As we got near to the end of the session, he seemed to get angrier and angrier. When we returned to the ward there was no word from his son. I asked for a message to be left for the son to contact me because I thought it could be useful to learn some more about Mr Mitchell's life. His new keyworker told me that she had heard that Mr Mitchell's wife had become an invalid and thereafter he slept in a chair alongside her bed. The son never got in touch with me. He visited less and less.

As I collected Mr Mitchell for the fifth session he started wailing in a way that felt like a complaint. When in my room he gave some really loud yells. I felt worried that anyone overhearing would wonder what on earth I was doing to him. I noticed, too, that he often shouted over me when I was talking to him. Eventually I realised he was angry with *me* for being handicapped because he couldn't get through to me. However much he shouted, I couldn't understand what he meant. He pulled his chair away to the wall and made just one attempt to move back, but couldn't because he had put the brake on one of the wheels. I felt near to tears and at the same time was aware of trying to distance myself from him. I talked about his pain and he got angry. I thought he felt I was humiliating him with pity. Later, I found myself thinking about his funeral. I said to him that I thought he wanted to die. He turned to me angrily and shouted very clearly 'No!' I replied that perhaps I hadn't understood his dilemma: he wanted to stay alive and wanted to die but he feared continuing to live and feared dying. He continued to shout angrily. I said I thought he might be worried about making me angry and that I would retaliate and hurt him in some way.

Towards the end of the session the decibels of Mr Mitchell's shouts escalated. I thought about how horrible it must be for him to now feel like his invalid wife. I remembered one son had not visited last week and the other son did not visit at all. I talked about him feeling I was abandoning him at the end of the session, like his loved ones. As I wheeled him out of the room I was shocked to realise I felt angry and cruel towards him.

At the sixth session I found Mr Mitchell in his pyjamas and in bed. His bed was one with twenty others in a corridor ward with beds on either side. A staff member told me Mr Mitchell had been sleepy and 'fighting' with them to go to bed. I pulled up a chair alongside the bed and drew the curtains around us. He lay with his eyes closed. From time to time his eyes flickered open, and just a few times he looked at me. I couldn't tell whether he wanted me to go or stay because he answered 'No' to every question. I decided to stay.

Sitting by his bedside for that half hour was one of the most excruciating experiences I have ever had. I became aware of all the impingements on him: television, radio, staff shouting to each other, relatives and staff talking and walking back and forth. I became conscious of how close the beds were to one another as one of the staff attending to an adjacent patient elbowed me through the curtains as she moved about on the other side. There was absolutely no privacy. Mr Mitchell lay quietly but once he shouted piercingly at me, giving me quite a shock. I began thinking that in his shouting Mr Mitchell was giving us some of his experience of having so much intrude on him, day in and day out, on this ward.

When he was quiet I felt I was sitting at the bedside of a dying man. I thought he might feel frightened of going to sleep in case he would not wake up, but I was unable to voice such a thought there on the ward.

At the eighth session, just three weeks before my summer holiday, Mr Mitchell's shirt was stained with food and he was not shaven. His shouts were especially piercing and frightening. I wondered if that was what the stroke felt like. I told Mr Mitchell about my holiday, how many weeks to go, how long I'd be away and when I would be back. He pulled his chair away and was quiet against the wall. He looked into the distance as if having a thought or a memory and then he cried out again. I said that when I was able to think about his pain then he seemed able to hold a thought in mind, but that brought its own pain: for a moment he was somewhere else, sometime else and then he was back with the pain and inconsolable grief of being here in hospital.

Just before the end of the session one of his slippers fell off. I asked him if he wanted me to put it back on. I thought he said yes. I put it back on his foot and as I prepared to wheel him back to the ward he held out his hand to me. I shook it. I felt very moved. When we entered the ward a nursing auxiliary, who was a temporary worker from an agency, shouted at Mr Mitchell, 'Do you want to go to bed?' and then 'Are you wet?' I felt most unhappy leaving him there.

When I entered the ward for the ninth session, the senior nurse told me in a sympathetic way that Mr Mitchell had a cold and was feeling miserable. I noticed his clothes because he was wearing a nice cardigan and a clean shirt. In my room, for the first time, he didn't pull his chair away but stayed sitting near me. He was quiet and appeared to be a bit drowsy but his eyes remained open. Occasionally he made some soft sounds as if to tell me he was still awake. Sometimes I thought he looked contemplative. Being with him felt peaceful. I wondered aloud if he felt sad and he seemed to say 'Aye?', so I repeated what I said. He seemed to agree. At one point he cried out, it seemed in anguish. I said it was painful to think and to remember and to be aware of where he is. And sad to think of what he has lost and that he will be losing me who gives him a hand, losing me during my holiday. Again he seemed to agree. As the end of the session drew near he became noisier. I talked about him feeling upset as we got near the end of the session and nearer to the holiday. He was quiet again as we returned to the ward.

After my holiday I saw Mr Mitchell the day before the twelfth session when he was brought to the patient and staff meeting on the ward. He looked spruce and clean then but the next day when I came to collect him for the session his clothes were stained with food. There was food still on his face and smeared over his wheel-chair. One of the auxiliaries wiped his face. I said we were going to my room. He shouted 'No!' and kept shouting as I wheeled him down the corridor. Perhaps this shouting was a protest about my absence over the holiday, but I felt unsure of its meaning. In the room he put the brake on his chair and stayed near me. For a while there was a feeling of a conversational flow between his noises and my talk. A couple of times he seemed to be trying to mouth some words. I couldn't understand him. Then he began wailing in an inconsolable way. I said 'You are sad today', and he replied very clearly 'Yes'. He became quiet and almost fell asleep.

A cat cried outside my window, wanting to get in. Mr Mitchell stirred. I said I thought he felt excluded and forgotten like the cat during my holiday. Perhaps he thought I might forget him again when the session ended. He was quiet for a while and then began wailing. I talked about what I thought he had lost in his life and the sadness and the pain. For a moment he looked searchingly into my eyes. Later, as we entered the ward he called out 'No!' and at that moment I too hated the ward. An auxiliary came up to us, greeting Mr Mitchell in a loud and cheerful voice. A senior staff member called me over to tell me Mr Mitchell had been 'up and down'.

At the sixteenth session the nurse who greeted me spoke warmly about Mr Mitchell but also complained of having worked for eight days without a break. In the session there was little contact with Mr Mitchell. I felt I must be mad to think he understood anything I was saying or got anything from the sessions. There was just no way of knowing. I kept looking at the clock, longing for the end of the session. I talked to him about time hanging heavily and then about him wanting to die. For a moment he looked at me angrily. I thought: 'So he has understood something I've said.' I then said, more kindly, that he was probably frightened of dying. He wiped his brow. I thought it must be such an effort for him to keep on going.

Later, my supervisor helped me think about what felt unbearable: Mr Mitchell's fear and terror and his existence which gets worse and worse, perhaps especially the not-knowing how long it will go on for. He wanted me to know how it feels. He was dealing with something that was driving him crazy. What do you do when your internal situation is intolerable and when you try to externalise it by putting it into others so they might understand, they too find it intolerable? How could I take him back to the ward after being with me in my quiet room: is it that I don't know what the ward is like or am I cruel?

In the seventeenth session he was quiet. He seemed extremely sad. I found my thoughts wandering away. I talked to him about how I thought he felt I could not bear to stay with his pain. He almost drifted off to sleep and, unusually, I felt sleepy. Occasionally he cried out as though he appeared to become aware of where he was, waking with a jolt, but into a living nightmare.

I noticed he moved his good arm as if to reach out to me. But I wasn't sure and didn't know whether to take his hand or not. Perhaps he was simply adjusting his position. However, it seemed different from before. I talked about him wanting to reach out to me and be held when he felt lonely. At the nineteenth session he again started moving his arm towards me, then putting it back on his lap or on the arm rest of his chair. I decided to take hold of his hand. He held my hand for a moment, as if wanting to pull me towards him and then he let it go. This happened several times. I said holding my hand was a bit of contact and he said 'Yeh', very clearly. After the halfway time in the session he abruptly pulled his chair away to the wall, something he had not done for some weeks. He started angrily shouting. I said that it was hard getting close when he felt I dropped him when I took him back to the ward. He seemed to agree but I wasn't sure. I began feeling I didn't understand anything as Mr Mitchell was getting angrier all the while.

In supervision I talked about how hard it was to know if anything I said to Mr Mitchell was right. My supervisor thought Mr Mitchell was leaving me in the dark perhaps because he felt I didn't need to be told or he might have been showing me how in the dark he felt. She said it was probably hard for him to keep in contact with me. She pointed out the vocabulary he and I were establishing through his different moods and gestures. I felt encouraged.

At the twenty-second session, just four weeks before my Christmas break, the ward sister told me Mr Mitchell had been very noisy during the day. Somewhat apologetically she said he should have been changed, meaning a soiled pad should have been removed. I said it must be uncomfortable for him. She replied that she doubted he could tell the difference but it would be unpleasant for me. There was food spilled over his clothing and a smell of incontinence. In my room he rocked himself back and forth in his chair, pulling himself upright then falling back, crossing and uncrossing his good leg over his paralysed one. He alternately shouted and groaned. I said I thought he was angry about being treated like a naughty baby and left in a soiled nappy. He didn't seem to react. After one very loud shout I thought he was about to weep and I was reminded of that first meeting when he had sobbed in my room.

I told Mr Mitchell about the Christmas holiday. He seemed to get angrier and kept looking away, ignoring whatever I said. Later, with just a few minutes left in the session he pushed his chair away. I noticed he used his good foot to propel his chair, whereas formerly he had used his arm. By the end of the session I was reeling from the smell in the room.

When I arrived to collect Mr Mitchell for the twenty-sixth session, the last before the Christmas holiday, the ward sister greeted me with some relief. She said Mr Mitchell had been very noisy all day. As I took him out of the ward one of the other patients muttered angrily about him. Mr Mitchell was unshaven but wearing a pleasantly patterned pullover. He shouted as we entered the room but did not move his chair away from me. I said I thought he was upset about the coming holiday. He became calm, making gentle sounds and sometimes looking drowsy. At one point he moved his hand towards me and I took it and held it for a moment, until he let it drop. He looked over at me from time to time and occasionally nodded off.

At the end of the session he put his foot on the floor and I could not move his chair. I said he didn't want to go. He kept his foot on the floor and I felt perplexed. I asked if he wanted his foot put on the footrest of the chair. He didn't respond but I put his foot on the footrest and took him back to the ward. The ward sister was surprised to see Mr Mitchell so quiet. I explained that he was upset about the holiday. She seemed interested by this explanation.

Following the Christmas break at the twenty-seventh session I found Mr Mitchell asleep in his chair. He woke as I approached his chair but I couldn't tell if he recognised me. I could only see two agency staff whom I didn't know. Once in my room he slept until the last ten minutes of the session. When he woke he rocked himself forward several times. I said I thought he was uncomfortable in the chair. He replied clearly 'Yeh'. I said that perhaps he was tired and fed up with me because of the holiday and also the move of the hospital in a few months' time. (I wondered to myself if he would survive the move.) He seemed to stir. I talked of time hanging very heavily. I wondered if he had felt he might not see me again and perhaps he thought he was dreaming when he first saw me today.

Just a few minutes before the end of the session he became agitated. I spoke of his awareness that there wasn't much time left, now in the session or in his life. He pushed his chair away with his foot in a defiant manner. As I tried to wheel him out of the room he put his foot down and stopped the chair. I said he was putting his foot down about not wanting to go. He lifted his foot and I took him back. He gave some quiet groans as we entered the ward.

At the twenty-eighth session one of the nurses told me Mr Mitchell was ill and had been refusing food. He wouldn't even eat his porridge, which was unusual for him and he had been quiet, not his usual self. She said another patient had died the previous night after having a fit. I sat by Mr Mitchell's bed with the curtains drawn around us. He was lying on his back, his mouth open and his eyes half closed. I noticed his very wrinkled neck. He was quiet. A nearby television intruded into my thoughts. I heard the actress Joan Collins being interviewed about her tips for keeping young and later some news about NHS closures and hospitals fighting to survive.

Mr Mitchell called out, at first somewhat quietly and then louder, as if to pull me back to him and remind me there was still some life in him. He became quiet again and I thought he was pleased I was there. I then worried he might die at any moment. I watched to see if he was still breathing. He stirred occasionally, I thought to show me he was alive. I talked about him feeling frightened of dying and uncomfortable to be alive, a terrible dilemma. I said he might have felt fed up with the hospital move ahead. He did not seem to react.

Sometimes he turned his head to look at me, I thought to see if I was still there or, perhaps, if he was. Sometimes he sounded angry and I wondered if he was angry to be still alive or angry to be giving up and dying. I thought he might feel I would be glad if he died but I felt that was a thought I coudn't voice in public on the ward. I thought he might be angry, too, about the constant intrusion of the television. There was no peace there.

Suddenly one of the nurses pulled the curtains open and then apologised when she saw me there. Perhaps she thought the curtains around the bed meant that Mr Mitchell had died. She also told me, in whispers, there had been another death on the ward and Mr Mitchell had not been well. Mr Mitchell seemed as if he was dozing off though he stayed awake. I said good-bye and that I would see him next week.

At the twenty-ninth session Mr Mitchell lay in his bed, his head propped up high on pillows. The senior nurse was giving Mr Mitchell something to drink from a beaker, she explained she wanted to get something down him. I pulled the curtains around the bed. I noticed traces of food on the sheets. Mr Mitchell's eyes were just partly open and there was some sticky secretion around his eyelids. His mouth was open and I could hear him breathing heavily. I thought of the phrase 'the breath of life'. It seemed hard for him to hold on and hard to let go, an enormous effort.

He kept moving his arm or leg, sometimes his lip, again I thought to let me know he was still alive. Just occasionally he turned to look at me. Then, in the latter half of the session, he did not look at me at all. He gave a few soft groans and that was all. Once more I wondered if he felt I was impatient for him to die but I felt I could not say it.

Amidst the usual noise of the ward I overheard an agency nurse auxiliary joking and later he abruptly pulled the curtains aside and then apologised. I had been told that Mr Mitchell's family were informed of his condition. Only one son visited.

When I said good-bye Mr Mitchell looked angrily at me and closed his eyes.

Five days later Mr Mitchell died. One of his sons was with him. The other son phoned the next day to complain to the staff that he had not been told. Both sons said they did not want any of Mr Mitchell's clothes or possessions from the ward. When I went to the ward, the sister and Mr Mitchell's keyworker were packing Mr Mitchell's belongings. The sister told me the sons didn't even want the nice framed photograph of Mr Mitchell's grandchildren. I watched her sadly taking Mr Mitchell's name label off his shaver and packing it to send to Oxfam. Mr Mitchell's keyworker, clearly distressed, said another patient was very upset to learn that Mr Mitchell had died because he used to get so angry with Mr Mitchell.

I felt a mixture of relief and sadness. I was relieved for him and for not having to see him again, but also I missed him.

Commentary

The early sessions show how difficult it was to think that Mr Mitchell could be frightened of me and could stir cruel feelings in me. I can see that I was soon drawn into cruel exchanges with him when I made interpretations about unconscious death wishes which clearly enraged him. There was probably some truth in these interpretations but I think they also conveyed my hatred of being with Mr Mitchell and my wish he would die.

My earlier work with Mr Mitchell's keyworker (reported at the end of Chapter 8) had uncovered the possibility that he was being abused on the ward. Despite the negative findings of the subsequent investigation, the question of whether he was abused and continued to be so remained inconclusive for me. My counselling experience with him, especially my counter-transference, suggested it was likely Mr Mitchell provoked abusive treatment. Perhaps the provocations were a result of abuse on the ward (and or even earlier abuse in his life) as a result of him identifying with the aggressor 'as a means of psychic survival' (Milton, 1994). Alternatively, the provocations may have been a reaction to the trauma of his strokes in which he drew abuse on to himself 'as a way of controlling the disturbance . . . to repeat the trauma in an assimilable experience and to omnipotently compensate for his handicap' (Sinason, writing about one of her handicapped patients, 1986, p. 150).

Despite my training in self-awareness I was still shocked to feel cruel towards a helpless old man. This experience was a salutory lesson about how upsetting it must be for care staff to experience similar feelings when working with patients like Mr Mitchell. His sometimes dishevelled, food-stained state was doubtless a reflection of his aggressiveness obstructing staff from cleaning him and of problems of staff shortages on the ward, but it probably also reflected conscious or unconscious punitiveness towards him because of his behaviour.

The session in which Mr Mitchell had been left so long in a soiled pad shows how cruelty can be inflicted by unthinking behaviour. It seems likely that this was in retaliation for his noisiness. Nursing and care staff are vulnerable to acting out negative feelings because it is usually regarded as unacceptable for them to have such feelings towards their patients. Peter Speck has described the 'chronic niceness' which can burden staff in a hospice (1994); and Vega Zagier Roberts has explained that 'In all caring work there are elements of uncaring', and the caring task

at times can be hateful . . . Obsessional routines of care can serve to protect patients from carers' unconscious hate, from what staff fear they might do to those in their charges if not controlled by rigid discipline. At the same time these routines can provide organisationally sanctioned ways of expressing hate of patients who exhaust, disgust or disappoint staff. (1994, p. 83).

Zagier Roberts has stressed that care staff need to be aware of their uncaring feelings as a safeguard against acting out these feelings towards their patients. Drawing on the work of Winnicott, Zagier Roberts makes the crucial observation that the capacity to tolerate hatred without expressing it depends on being 'thoroughly aware of one's hate' (1994, p. 83). To achieve this kind of awareness care staff need training programmes and support structures which permit them to acknowledge such feelings.

I came to realise that from Mr Mitchell's point of view I was disabled because I could not understand him. I see, too, that I tended to become slow and handicapped as I identified with Mr Mitchell. For example, in the fourth session I was unable to make the obvious connection between the son not visiting that day and his withdrawal during the session. It took me another week to bear the pain of making the link and speaking about it in the session. The absence of Mr Mitchell's family may be understandable because of the pain of seeing him reduced to such a dreadful condition. Nonetheless, as Peter Hildebrand has pointed out, 'The intervention of the state has not helped here, since for so many the fact that it will supply an old people's home for their dependent relatives offers them the chance to avoid the working through of their feelings and attitudes to their parents in their later years' (1995, p. 93). I wonder if my own intervention by seeing Mr Mitchell did not hasten his family's withdrawal because they felt less need to visit.

The sessions leading up to the holidays illustrate developments that can be achieved in work of this kind. Being at Mr Mitchell's bedside helped me understand more about the constant impingements he endured on the ward and how, perhaps, his shouting was conveying something of that experience. My staying alongside his bed must have meant a lot to him because the following week, the seventh session, he stayed longer sitting by me before retreating to the wall and there was more of a conversational flow. The next session he appeared more able to hold a thought in his mind because I think he felt more held in my mind. The experience of simply being with someone, resisting the urge to do anything, is comparable to the maternal holding that Esther Bick (see Chapter 1) described as so important for the infant, because it can enable an elderly patient like Mr Mitchell to feel that his fragmented and chaotic experience can be gathered together in another person's mind.

The episode of the dropped slipper indicates the value, for patients and carers, of looking for meaning in tiny pieces of behaviour which might otherwise go unnoticed or be dismissed as irrelevant or mere chance. Mr Mitchell's slipper had not fallen off before but its falling-off followed the news of my holiday. Neither had Mr Mitchell held his hand out to me before. The slipper was like a metaphor for a feeling of being dropped by me during the holiday, just as holding out his hand could be a way of letting me know he felt I was giving him a hand. He expressed a closeness to me the next week when he did not move his chair but sat by me throughout the session; not only did he look better dressed and cared for, but the nurse seemed more sympathetic towards him. Sinason has written: 'Understanding or trying to understand meaning does not necessarily make disturbance or aggressive behaviour go away, but it can lessen the extent of the damage to our clients and make us and our colleagues feel more able to bear the difficulties' (1992, p. 227).

The news of the second holiday shows further evidence of Mr Mitchell's understanding and how he could expand his range of expressiveness, this time literally putting his foot down about the holiday. The reports of Mr Mitchell's anger on the ward suggest that some of the anger stirred by the holiday was being expressed on the ward. Perhaps I could have done more to gather his anger into the transference to try to ease the situation on the ward. Alternatively, it may be that at this juncture of his life, Mr Mitchell needed to resort to this kind of splitting in order to preserve something good in the sessions and inside himself.

I think my reluctance to talk about dying when I was with Mr Mitchell on the ward reflects the pressure against thinking or speaking about such topics on the wards. Though death was a common experience it was nonetheless a difficult subject for staff to discuss. However, the ward sister's obvious interest when I made a connection between Mr Mitchell's aggressiveness and my holiday makes me aware of how relatively little contact I had with the staff on Mr Mitchell's ward. Although I conducted weekly patient and staff meetings, few staff attended and generally I felt there was little access to the staff. I could see that the staff felt appreciative of the interest I showed in Mr Mitchell. But in so far as I might have been able to make better contact and didn't, I feel I perpetuated an unhelpful distance between the staff and myself. I now think that regular discussions about my work with Mr Mitchell would have been a way of supporting the work and the staff.

The developments in the work helped Mr Mitchell, myself and his carers to be more in touch with his misery and his depressive feelings (see Chapter 1) and less consumed by his persecution. But I can now see that as Mr Mitchell became sadder I found it hard to bear his grief, and at times my interpretations took him away from sad feelings. For example, in session thirteen he appeared to be singing me a sad song, making a contact with me which I eventually broke by my interpretations about him wanting to die and of feeling hopeless. It was especially difficult to be aware of the comfort he felt from being with me, the pain he experienced as we approached the end of the sessions and then feel guilty about taking him back to the ward. However, talking about the link between approaching the end of the sessions and Mr Mitchell's increasing anguish at times seemed to help both him and me to bear the feelings. What was brought home to me was the pain of helping someone like Mr Mitchell stay in touch with sad and sorrowful feelings, almost as though being persecuted by his shouting was preferable for both of us.

I think the outcome of these developments was that Mr Mitchell was enabled to face his death, let go of life and die. The two holiday breaks focused the grieving work. Because Mr Mitchell could not speak it was not possible to know about how he experienced loss. But having established some contact with him I was then able to help him mourn my loss and implicity other losses revived for him in the transference. When I could bear the pain of his sad, depressive feelings, then he felt held by me and could begin to let go. Holding his hand out to me, letting me hold it and dropping it, conveyed this process of being held and letting go. As well, his sleepiness in the later sessions and my corresponding drowsiness seemed an indication of him beginning to withdraw from his attachments. Hence this work had perhaps facilitated his anticipatory mourning for the end of his life (see Chapter 3, the work with Mrs Taylor, and Judd, 1989).

Mr Mitchell was on tranquillising medication, but I don't think the sleepiness could be explained solely by that because it seemed he was still quite active, troublingly so, on the wards. I was unhappy about the use of tranquillisers, and yet also sympathetic to the plight of the staff and other patients who found Mr Mitchell's shouting intolerable. I felt unable to intervene about the medication.

In the last weeks of his life, Mr Mitchell's refusal to eat seemed an active expression of his wish to die, a phenomenon I had by then become familiar with in these elderly patients. The final sessions at Mr Mitchell's bedside show the difficulty of trying to stay in contact with him and at the same time allow him to withdraw. The most useful contribution seemed simply being with him, whereas when I offered interpretations I felt I was intruding on him. Essentially the task became to allow Mr Mitchell to take his leave of me and die, which meant offering an unobtrusive attachment he could relinquish.

Supervision was crucial in enabling me to stay with the work, to process some of my own difficult emotions and particularly to feel that my distress was being held and understood. Supervision helped me to keep in mind that some of my tormented feelings were possibly also a communication of Mr Mitchell's torment. It also helped me to recall the achievements in the work which I think is often a problem for these elderly patients: how to stay in touch with their achievements in the face of the frustrations of physical and mental decline. In a discussion with my supervisor about the final sessions, she commented on the nurses' valuable skill in recognising when a patient is dying, a skill that often goes unacknowledged and unappreciated. The way the nursing and care staff were left to deal with Mr Mitchell's death is unfortunately typical of the way responsibility for the old and dying are displaced on to these staff by a society that wants little to do with death.

Finally, I have been asked why I chose to work with Mr Mitchell who could not speak. On reflection, I think I felt identified with his inability to express himself, an aspect of myself which I became aware of in my own therapy. I realise how invaluable it was to have someone there for me, endeavouring to put into words what I could not say.

Working with Care Staff and the Elderly

6

THEORETICAL UNDERPINNING OF THE INSTITUTIONAL WORK

Introduction

Psycho-analysts, psychiatrists and social scientists with a psycho-analytic orientation have made important advances in the understanding of how institutions work and how unconscious processes affect organisational life. Their understandings have been successfully applied to bring about beneficial changes in a wide variety of commercial and public service organisations, by practitioners taking up the role of *organisational consultants*. This chapter presents an introduction to some of the insights which have emerged from this work and some of the similarities and differences between a consultancy and a counselling or therapeutic role.

(For the reader who is interested in pursuing these ideas, see Obholzer and Zagier Roberts, 1994.)

Understanding institutions and organisational consultancy

I would like to describe a pioneering study of a nursing service in a general hospital by Isabel Menzies Lyth (1960) to illustrate some of the psycho-analytical understandings about institutions. These insights about nursing are still relevant and the understandings of organisations have wide application.

Menzies Lyth's study followed a request from a hospital for help with developing new methods for organising the allocation of student nurses. Her team conducted an intensive research programme, interviewing staff individually and in groups, feeding back preliminary findings and gathering further information. As the study progressed what emerged was the importance of under-standing the very high level of anxiety in the nurses. There was anxiety associated with carrying out the primary nursing task of looking after the patients who were too ill to be cared for at home; and anxiety about having to get on with other colleagues whilst doing this. The study also revealed unconscious sources of anxiety because of what close physical contact with the patient's illnesses and injuries stir up in the nurses' internal worlds. Early phantasies are revived from infancy, in which the infant's destructive feelings are experienced as injurious attacks on internal and external objects. Anxieties arise because of the close correspondence between the nurses' external situation and phantasies they trigger. Additionally, nurses are receptacles for the patients' and relatives' conscious and unconscious feelings, for example about fears of dying, or disgust with physical illness and treatment.

Menzies Lyth observed that faced with these anxieties, collec-tively the staff of an institution (both consciously and uncon-sciously) organise their work partly with the purpose of managing the anxieties in what become *defensive social systems*. These systems may be adaptive and appropriate to pursuing the institution's primary task, or may be maladaptive, resistant to change and at odds with the motives for which the staff joined the institution. However, the social systems become real parts of institutions, can affect the personality structure of those who work within them and new members of an institution will be required to adapt to them or leave. The social systems reflected early defences against anxiety, such as splitting and projective identification. For example, there was a 'splitting up' of the nurse–patient relationship in the way nurses related to patients primarily by the tasks they had to perform on them, which ensured there was little continuity in the nurse and patient contact. Nurses were encouraged to maintain an attitude of detachment. They rarely got to know their patients, who were more often referred to by their illnesses or bed number than by name.

Menzies Lyth drew attention to the way that the nurses' roles were often diminished by a projective process in which responsi-bility was projected upwards into superiors and irresponsibility was projected downwards into subordinates. Junior, less experienced and less trained staff were treated as irresponsible in all kinds of subtle ways: for example, in the tone of voice a superior might use to say 'I'll do that.' This meant that incompetence or uncertainty could be projected into junior staff and some of their competence could be 'filched' from them. Projection of responsibility upwards, though relieving of anxiety, meant that competence and skills were also lost by being attributed to superiors in this way. The projective process often left a vacuum in which nurses were very unsure of just what they could be doing, and meant what they were doing was well below their capability. The senior staff, though firmly in control and full of projected competence, were frequently overwhelmed with tasks that more junior colleagues could appropriately have performed.

The social systems in the hospital were seen to be ways of avoiding anxiety, by, for example, not having continuous contact with patients or by not having a sense of responsiblity for the work. The result of these defences was that nurses were then prevented from overcoming the anxieties in more constructive ways. In some respects the work was less stressful, but also less demanding or developing of their capacities, and therefore produced other stresses. Above all, these defences frustrated the nurses' motivations for choosing such work, because entering this profession implies a wish to overcome these anxieties by reparative work. Facing the anxieties means there is a chance to sort out the external situation from the internal phantasies provoked by it. Involvement in reparative activity also supports inner confidence in the strength of loving feelings and in the capacity to restore the internal world.

Working with the institution in a consultative role has parallels with a therapeutic role. In particular, the analytically trained organisational consultant brings skills of : 'evenly suspended attention', meaning avoiding preconceptions about what is important or not important, (Menzies Lyth, 1988, quoting Freud); encouraging the clients to talk freely, not just about 'the problem' but about whatever else occurs to them in a free associative way; and listening as much to what is *not* said as to what is said (Bain, 1982). As far as possible the consultant tries to have an attitude of not-knowing so that what is unknown might emerge. The consultant tries to avoid being the expert with the answers in order to give the clients the responsibility for finding their own solutions.

In organisational consultation there is a strong emphasis on gathering together all the available information to help identify the problem, bearing in mind that what is initally presented as 'the problem' might not be the central issue. It may be a matter of enabling members of the institution to say what otherwise cannot be said or only spoken about in certain groups or sub-groups. But often, as Menzies Lyth describes, there is a situation in which a deep source of distress may be unconscious and may be dispersed by being split into fragments. These fragments of distress are projected by members of the institution into different aspects of the work and environment, which are then believed to constitute 'the problem'. For example, there may be complaints about particular working conditions which, though having some substance, when addressed fail to alleviate the underlying source of anxiety. The consultant can gain access to the unconscious anxieties by offering holding and containment (see Chapter 1) to the institution, in enabling the clients to project unconscious feelings about the problem into the consultant role. As in the therapeutic process, this is a repetitive task: containment, which may lead to understanding and resolution of some aspects of the problem, has to be offered over and over again. The consultant has to withstand the pressure to be all-knowing and the attacks which come when he is felt to be withholding his knowledge. In this way he has to *work through* the resolution of the problems with the clients and enable them to take back projections, so that they can continue to solve problems and work creatively after he has gone.

The consultant needs to keep in mind *the technical and social structure* of the institution, *the roles* of individuals within it and the particular *work culture*. There will be technical aspects to the structure which relate to the task of the institution, its 'input' and 'output', its relation to external organisations and its internal organisation, as well as social groupings of its members, all of which will affect its running. There will also be the formal roles to which staff are allocated and projective processes which influence the content of those roles, as revealed in the Menzies Lyth study. The kind of conscious and unconscious feelings staff experience in relation to the work contribute to the work culture. All of these different aspects are interconnected, so that working for change in any one area will be dependent on another. For example, only addressing staff attitudes will not be enough to bring about change without working with the implications for staff roles and the structure of the organisation. Change, however much wanted, is likely to be resisted because it means giving up the familiar, experiencing the unknown and having to learn from new experience. Further, if the work is to draw on more capacity of the staff it will probably be more difficult and stressful, even though ultimately more rewarding.

One of the difficulties of working as an organisational consultant or as a counsellor within an institution is the social contact with the client group. Psychodynamic work needs some distance to examine the transference and counter-transference in order to reflect on the unconscious processes. There is also a need to examine the effects of the social contact on the work.

In institutions for the care of the elderly, carers are especially vulnerable to unconscious anxieties associated with death and destruction because their work involves close contact with damaged and dying patients. Moreover, some of these elderly patients present particular difficulties because of their destructive and angry feelings and their envy of their able-bodied, younger helpers. Hence, the organisations in which this care takes place are liable to erect various institutional defences against these anxieties which may actually obstruct the reparative work that the carers wish to do for their patients. The defensive systems may contribute to the institutionalisation of the patients, especially in producing passivity and decline which could mistakenly be attributed to organic or physical causes (Martindale, 1989b). It is easy to be drawn into a preoccupation with an elderly patient's severe physical problems and to concentrate help on what can be done to alleviate the symptoms, thus overlooking the patient's internal world (Davenhill, 1991). I find it very hard to know how much an elderly patient's difficulties are a result of physical impairment consequent upon illness and ageing, or how much the patients' and carers' emotional reactions to illness and ageing contribute to the patients' physical, mental and emotional decline. The next section introduces some concepts I have found useful in thinking about this problem.

Psycho-analytic work with handicap and disability

Over the last fifteen years there has been an increase in psychotherapeutic work by psycho-analytically trained therapists with mentally handicapped adults and children who suffer from severe emotional difficulties. Many of these patients are also partially or severely physically disabled. This work has led to important developments in the understanding of handicap, whether physical, mental or emotional. Valerie Sinason (1992) has written, beautifully and movingly, about the work in a book based on a psychotherapy and research workshop at the Tavistock clinic. Her book furthers understanding of the struggle we can all experience when trying not to 'spoil or handicap' our basic constitutional inheritance. She distinguishes between primary and secondary handicap. *Secondary handicap* is a defensive elaboration of the primary difficulties and can mean 'attacking intact skills and intelligence' because of the pain of facing the original handicap.

I think there are direct parallels between the experiences of the mentally and physically handicapped and the elderly who suffer mental and physical disability and who are therefore vulnerable to the various forms of secondary handicap that Sinason has described. She reports her work with an elderly man suffering from Alzheimer's Disease, and at various points in her book draws parallels with the elderly. She also reports a study by Wright of mute children which showed that a fifth of them did not speak because of an underlying speech or language handicap. This study reminded me of elderly patients who are reluctant to speak because of speech impairments following a stroke. It made me wonder about various forms of secondary handicap which afflict the elderly but which can go unnoticed by being attributed to organic causes or simply to being old.

Secondary handicap can involve mild handicap, opportunistic handicap, or sometimes psychotic defences against trauma. *Mild handicap* is most often seen in the smile of the handicapped person which does not express genuine happiness but is intended to keep others happy. The handicapped person's smile perpetrates the belief that the child or adult has no intelligence and is therefore not aware of their disability. Sinason quotes Jon Stokes, also at the Tavistock, as drawing attention to the distinction between '*cognitive intelligence and emotional intelligence*', meaning that even though a patient may show no signs of intelligence he can still have an emotional capacity for experiencing and understanding. To make contact with this emotional intelligence requires the overcoming of a lot of guilt, the patient's guilt about being handicapped and the worker's guilt about being normal. Sinason painfully discovered that the twisted physical postures in which her handicapped patients seemed trapped by their organic impairment were often forms of mild secondary handicap. The twisted postures served to exaggerate the handicap and hide the true state of a patient. When the pain and unhappiness of the primary handicap could be understood then patients sometimes gave up some of the grotesque distortions of their bodies; and when there was no longer a need to provide false reassurances by smiling and they could instead be sad and angry, handicapped patients often revealed significant advances in their speech and intelligence.

Sinason gives a vivid illustration of removing the 'leaves' of mild secondary handicap in the way she responded to the frequent question from her patients of 'You all right?' This is a form of greeting I frequently encountered from staff and patients in the long-stay hospital. Sinason understood that in this form of address her patients were telling her they were not all right but they doubted that she could bear to know. They also felt the need to appease her, or their parents or carers, for being handicapped. By not replying 'yes', she describes how it is possible to give the patient a space in which to express his not-all-right feelings of sadness and anger.

Opportunistic secondary handicap is where the destructive aspects of a patient's personality join in with the disability. Sinason describes an example of a patient whose hatred, envy and a major primary handicap resulted in violent outbursts against his carers. She also describes *psychotic defences against trauma*, especially the trauma of physical and sexual abuse, which can result in patients dismantling their mind and capacities in order not to see, hear or remember the abuse they suffered. One of her patients, following long and difficult therapeutic work in which he revealed details of sexual abuse and also considerable ability and insight, said 'Being stupid is being mad.' There had been no one who could bear to know about his abuse and he had retreated from his own painful awareness into a smiling idiot state. Sinason reminds us that the original meaning of 'stupid' is 'numbed with grief', which well captures the pain behind the secondary handicap. There is, too, an aggressive component to the handicapped smile because, if we are taken in by it, we are stupid and are being laughed at.

Sinason mentions the atmosphere of cheerfulness which pervades homes for the elderly in which they, like the mentally handicapped, are encouraged to smile and be happy. As she says, it is very difficult to express anger when you are dependent on your carers and can fear abandonment and even death itself. It can feel a hostile environment because, as with the mentally handicapped, there can be *conscious and unconscious death wishes* against these elderly patients. Carers – families, friends or staff – and disabled elderly patients themselves can very naturally feel they would be better off dead than alive, having lost much of what makes life worth living. Society, too, seems to complain of the elderly living longer, increasing in numbers, consuming more and more resources and being 'dumped' in health services by uncaring relatives. Little wonder that some of the disabled elderly might withdraw into mindless inert states, expressing their anger by destroying what remains of their intellectual and physical capacities.

Sinason describes how workers can become 'stupid', beaming back at the smile which conceals loss and abuse, because of the pain of recognising the grief and the helplessness to do anything about it.

There is also a tendency to want to infantilise the handicapped (Bicknell, 1983), including the disabled elderly, because of the discomfort of acknowledging the adult who is reduced to such a humiliating state. Mannoni (1967), also quoted by Sinason (1992), sees addressing patients in a way that requires no response as a way in which carers can express their murderous feelings and their wish to keep the patient in sick role.

It is often very difficult for carers to think about the meaning of violent or aggressive behaviour in disabled patients because of the unbearable feelings underlying such behaviour. It is more usual to attribute the violence to some organic cause or a long-standing personality problem. It has been suggested that the rages in patients suffering from cerebral palsy may be more a reaction to the attitudes of their carers than their palsy (Freeman, quoted by Sinason). Aggression is necessary for the infant or toddler to master his world and move beyond the restrictions of his cot or playpen (Spitz, quoted by Sinason). But, for the elderly handicapped patient deteriorating into an ever restricted life, with cot sides around his bed and straps to hold him into a wheelchair, aggressive outbursts can only convey his impotence. Finally, Sinason adds a sobering caution that 'understanding or trying to understand' does not necessarily mean that the disturbing behaviour will cease. Understanding can decrease the damage that such secondary handicap can inflict on these patients and can make their difficulties more bearable for the carers, but 'sometimes too much damage is done, organically or emotionally, for treatment to make major changes' (p. 228).

7

OBSERVATION OF A LONG-STAY WARD FOR THE ELDERLY

Introduction

There were five long-stay wards in the hospital, each had twenty-one beds. The majority of patients were in their seventies or eighties and had multiple illnesses which left them severely disabled and highly dependent. Most were wheelchair-bound; just a very few could walk, but only with the help of the staff. Nearly half had suffered from strokes and a third from dementia. A smaller proportion had rheumatoid arthritis, epilepsy, fractures or diabetes. Some had speech impairments or were unable to speak, or eat or swallow. Many were incontinent. Nearly a fifth had hearing and visual problems. Few were terminally ill, but all would remain in long stay care until they died. Several had been on the wards for over ten years.

My first impressions of the hospital were of long corridor 'Nightingale' wards, suffused with plastic flowers which never die. There was an office for staff at one end, and a day-room at the other, where mostly female patients sat, making no contact, sometimes slumped sleeping, or staring into space, opposite a television showing a children's programme which no one watched. Each time I entered the hospital I was hit by the smell of incontinence, which lingered despite the best efforts to disguise or remove it.

In this chapter I shall describe an observational study which I supervised of one of the long-stay wards. It was conducted by Graham Thompson who was on a four months' placement with me as part of the training for an MSc in clinical psychology. Graham had been on two previous clinical placements. He was in his late twenties. Before taking post-graduate training he had done some travelling and had some other work experience. Of slight build and with a gentle, unassuming manner, Graham impressed me with his warmth and sensitivity. Patients and staff used to speak to me about him in a friendly way as my 'young man', which made me feel quite old and quite paternal.

When Graham came for a first visit I took him around one of the long-stay wards, introducing him to some of the patients. As we spoke to the patients I was embarrassed to become aware of myself talking loudly in a too-cheerful voice. Graham's first impressions of the hospital were a salutary reminder to me of what I realised I had already become immured against: the shock, confusion, bewilderment, helplessness and, as he said, 'the relentless pain'.

I arranged for Graham to visit one of the wards at the same time and day each week for an hour, as an observer. The patients on the ward were a typical cross-section of those in the long-stay hospital. The model of observation was based on psycho-analytic observations of mothers and infants (see Rustin, 1989) and had also been used in a recently published study of another geriatric hospital (McKenzie-Smith, 1992). Graham was to sit with the patients in their day-room. He was not to take any notes at the time or to initiate any activity. He was there to observe what happened, including his own emotional responses. After the observations he was to write up detailed, blow-by-blow accounts of what he remembered and what he felt, and to bring these 'process recordings' for discussion in weekly supervision. His feelings, or counter-transference, were an important source of information with which we could study the emotional experience of the patients and staff on the ward.

I hope this chapter will set the scene for the insitutional setting in which I worked with staff and patients. I hope, too, it will show the value of listening to these elderly patients.

The observations of a long-stay ward

Note how hard it was for the observer to take in the illness, disability, withdrawal and passivity of the patients in the day-room. However, note that as he listened to the patients they were able to express their grief, especially as their grieving feelings were galvanised by his holiday and then the ending of his visits.

At the first observation, the ward manager (whom Graham had previously met) took him to the day-room where she introduced him to the patients. As an aside to Graham she divided the patients into those who were 'disabled', the 'sensible' ones and the 'goodies'. Graham took up a chair alongside one of the 'sensible' ones, Thelma, who told Graham she had been on the ward for five years. Later, Zoe was wheeled in, and was placed alongside Thelma. The two women chatted to each other and included Graham in their conversation. It was to become an established pattern that Graham would sit with these two women whom he described, with a laugh, as 'the two gossips'. During the observation he felt impressed with the ordinariness of it all.

At the second observation, as Graham was sitting with Thelma waiting for Zoe to arrive, she said to him 'Isn't Zoe full of life!' She then spoke briefly about having had two strokes which she said were like a 'prison sentence'. Zoe was brought in by two of the female staff, who were laughing and making jokes to Graham with a sexual innuendo. Graham said Zoe's arrival was like a 'fiesta'.

Later, Graham noticed another woman patient who appeared about to break into laughter but who then spoke in a bizarre way about 'ghosts in the garden', seeming to refer to a son who had died. Thelma and Zoe spoke in a kindly way to her, reassuring her it was 'not her fault'. There followed a long silence during which Graham said he could hear the knitting one woman was doing.

Then Thelma talked of the recreation ward. She used to enjoy going there to take part in the activities, but not any more. She'd stopped going. Graham noticed that Zoe, too, was less cheerful. In another part of the room a woman who looked very frail mumbled quietly to herself. Then an 'orderly' came in to prepare tables for lunch. Graham felt easier about leaving than the previous week. Zoe said 'I'll see you next week' and Thelma gave him a 'knowing glance'.

When Graham arrived for the third observation there were relatives of one of the male patients, Dave, visiting in the day-room. Graham felt embarrassed and wondered what these visitors would think of him being there. He was glad when they soon left. Thelma and Zoe were not present. Graham wondered where they were. For the first time he felt bored. After half an hour there was still no sign of his 'friends', Thelma and Zoe. He feared they might have died but reassured himself they couldn't have died because their tables were still there.

Graham noticed that one of the women he'd seen before had a special writing pad for messages and then appreciated that she must be deaf. He felt stupid not to have realised it before. A staff member was writing words on the pad for the woman. Then Zoe was brought in and talked to Graham. She said she'd come into hospital against her will. She was angry and blamed her daughter because it was boring all day here on the ward. She said she'd been a bit 'funny in the head' but had recovered. She kept laughing as she was telling Graham these things and, referring to the laughing, she said, 'It's a habit.' Her daughter visited every evening. Zoe said she thought her daughter was 'probably trying to make it up' to her for letting her down by not looking after her at home.

Later, Thelma was wheeled in. She said she'd been having her hair done. Graham said he'd wondered where she was. She replied it was nice that someone wondered where they were. Graham told them he would be on holiday in two weeks' time and would return after a month. Zoe and Thelma then spoke as if he was about to go on holiday straight away. They didn't seem to expect any advance warning. Afterwards, Graham said he found it difficult to leave that day.

At the fourth observation Graham was struck by how lifeless and tedious it felt in the day-room. Nothing seemed to change. Then he noticed a new patient in a chair with a sign above it saying 'Nil by mouth'. The chair had a plastic cushion on its seat. Graham wondered if this meant that the new patient was incontinent. Graham saw that all the lunch things were already out on the tables. It was only 11 o'clock. A staff member looked in and said to him it was a 'mad house' today.

After half an hour Thelma was brought in. She said it was 'hectic, not many staff today'. The new patient appeared worried and seemed to be looking for her box of tissues. Thelma called out, 'Have you lost your box?' and the woman said 'Yes'. Zoe came in and didn't appear to see Graham. She asked the carer to put her in a different position which was some distance away from Graham. Then she noticed Graham and said: 'Not seeing you next week.' Graham reminded her that it was the week after next he would not be there. She asked 'Will you miss us?' and answered her question 'Not really, no'. Graham tried to nod that he would. For the rest of the observation she talked to Thelma in a way that made Graham feel left out of their conversation.

The new patient burst into tears. A staff member came in and started joking about the ladies 'chatting up this young man'. Then the new patient started talking to Graham but he had difficulty understanding her because her dentures kept slipping. As Graham listened to her, she settled and had less trouble with the dentures. He began to understand she was talking about having lost her husband and her son. The carer, who was nearby, said rather impatiently to Graham that it was ten years ago that the patient's husband died and she had been 'going on about it' for some time. Thelma and Zoe looked on rather disapprovingly. When it was time to go Thelma and Zoe said they'd see Graham next week and, seeming to want to reassure him, one of them said 'We'll be OK.'

At the fifth observation, when Graham arrived Thelma was knitting. Graham noticed another patient sitting there looking old and withered. He was struck by how old this woman looked and the room seemed emptier than usual. Thelma was pensive. She started reminiscing about her parents. She recalled her father buying her a pony for a pony trap and she emphasised that the trap showed how long ago it was. She talked of missing her garden. Then, looking at the flowers on her table, she said they were dead. She said that she couldn't go anywhere on her own now. She seemed to be trying to stop herself from crying. She said she couldn't concentrate any more, that she used to write and go to activities, but she didn't any more. She was obviously irritated by the television in the room which seemed to be always on.

Zoe was brought in with the new 'Nil by mouth' patient who seemed calmer. Three members of staff lifted Zoe into her chair and then left. Graham felt his attention was now divided between the three women, Thelma, Zoe and the new patient, Iris. Zoe showed Graham a photograph of herself in the activities ward with a young man whom she described as a 'temporary helper'. Then a young female carer came in and talked with Graham in a rather flirtatious way.

Iris became upset. Zoe spoke comfortingly to her. The young staff member looked uneasy and left abruptly. Iris said she was upset about losing her husband and not seeing enough of her son. Rather crossly, she said it wasn't much of a life here.

Graham felt the time passed quickly. When he got up to go, Zoe said they wouldn't be seeing him next week and Thelma said 'Have a nice time.'

At the sixth observation, after the holiday, Graham looked forward to going back to the ward. The staff seemed to be expecting him. The day-room was very busy, with a lot of patients in it. Graham pulled up his chair alongside Thelma. She scarcely spoke to him. Graham gradually began to feel let down and disappointed.

Thelma got angry with another patient, a very large woman whose male visitor was sitting blocking the television. A domestic came in and was irritated with some of the patients, telling them crossly 'I'm not a nurse!' She then stood with the male visitor blocking the television. One of the women patients kept saying 'Dear, oh dear'.

Zoe was brought in and Graham was relieved because she looked pleased to see him. But then she appeared to ignore Graham deliberately as she proceeded to talk to Thelma. The television was visible again and Graham began to find the morning programme grating on him. He felt miserable. Zoe became quiet and eventually fell asleep. Graham felt it was all futile. He noticed one of the women who seemed uncomfortable in her chair and he thought there was no release for her. He wondered why these patients bothered to stay alive in these conditions. Iris was not there. He hoped she might come and bring some life. When it was time for him to leave Thelma said she would let Zoe know, but then Zoe woke and warmly said good-bye to him. Graham left feeling they hadn't missed him.

At the seventh observation Thelma seemed brighter and asked Graham about his family. When Graham said his sisters were both abroad, Thelma said how she would love to travel. Zoe was quieter than usual but friendly to Graham. Thelma told Graham she had had a dream in which she wanted to play football but could only afford a small tennis ball which meant that she lost the game. After the account of the dream the ward cat came into the day-room. They talked about the cat for a while and then fell silent for the rest of the time.

At the eighth observation Thelma was talkative until Zoe arrived, then they were both quiet. Graham found himself feeling sleepy and bored. At the end of the time he felt bad tempered and tired.

At the final, ninth observation Thelma was not present because she was having her hair done. The domestic positioned Zoe some distance away from Graham. Zoe said to Graham, 'Oh well, you're off soon.' Again there was little contact with Graham. A couple of staff came in, joking with some of the patients, and one said sarcastically to Graham 'Haven't you any work to do?'

When Graham said good-bye Zoe asked 'Will I see you again?' Graham said he thought probably not. Zoe replied 'What a shame, you'll miss me.' As he was leaving the ward manager asked Graham if had learned anything. Another staff member said, with a laugh, 'You know he sits there doing nothing.'

Commentary

I think the early observations show the pressure in the ward to deny the extent of the patients' illnesses and disabilities. For example, the ward manager's categories for the patients implied that only one group was 'disabled', whereas in reality all the patients were in hospital because of the severity of their disabilities. The denial can also be seen in the way Graham positioned himself with two of the 'sensible', gossiping patients, joining them in a portrayal of 'ordinariness' which denied the physical and mental decline which surrounded him. It was as if the rest of patients in the day-room, most of whom were mute and inert and in various states of deterioration, were invisible to Graham. His observations were in sharp contrast to his first impressions when he felt shocked, illustrating how quickly defences can be erected against the pain on these wards.

In the second observation the atmosphere of festivity suggests a manic excitement as another form of denial to lift staff and patients over the sad feelings. However, I think because of the presence of the observer who could begin to listen and think about the patients' feelings, the patients seemed enabled to voice some of their grief. This doubtless reflects a shift in the observer who had had the support of supervision to help him digest his experience, which is indicative of the support care staff need if they are to allow their patients to express painful feelings. Nonetheless, the difficulty in thinking about the pain in the patients' lives is apparent again in Graham's sudden embarrassment about what the visitors thought about him being there, in contrast to his attitude towards the patients, as though the patients had no thoughts or capacity to think about his presence. I feel it is often too painful to appreciate that these elderly patients still have thoughtful and emotional lives whilst they endure so much loss.

The patients' reactions to Graham's holiday illustrate the strong feelings which can be evoked by absences of carers, whether staff or family. As well as experiencing feelings of loss which are particular to the carer who is absent, the absence is also a reminder of feelings and memories, conscious and unconscious, about other losses which these elderly people have experienced and further losses they anticipate; and finally the loss of their own lives. The material about Graham's holiday shows how important it can be for these elderly people to have an opportunity to feel understood and work through some of the feelings about loss. Sitting with the patients and listening, as Graham did, can be an opportunity for the carers to learn more about their patients' feelings. In particular, in the fourth observation it seemed the new patient was expressing some grief on behalf of all the patients there, when she cried about losing her son and husband. When Graham listened to her it was clear she felt held by him and more able to make herself understood. However, the staff's jokes and Thelma and Zoe's obvious disapproval show how unwelcome any expression of grief was on the ward. I felt that Thelma and Zoe were probably also frightened that Graham would not like the new patient being distressed and that he might not come back, so they reassured him *they* would be 'OK' as he left the ward. I thought that Zoe's sitting away from Graham, and then Thelma and Zoe excluding Graham from their conversation, were reactions to the news of his holiday. When Zoe and Thelma left Graham out of their conversation, they gave him a taste of how they felt hurt and left out.

In the fifth observation, as Graham noticed how *old* one of the patients was and the emptiness in the room, he seemed more in touch with the elderly state of these patients and the emptiness of their lives. Thelma expressed the consequent dilemma of either being driven back into reminiscences of her garden or facing the encroaching reality of death which she alluded to when talking about the dead flowers on her table. It was as though death was all there was left. I thought Zoe's photograph of herself and the 'temporary helper' was also an unconscious acknowledgement of the help it was having Graham taking an interest in them and of Graham's temporary status, that he was soon to leave them. The young female staff member introduced a flirtatious sexuality which I think was an attempt to excite and distract staff and patients from the sad feelings which were voiced very clearly by the new patient, Iris. At that point I think the staff member found it unbearable and left Graham to deal with the distress.

In the observation after Graham's return from holiday there was a conspicuous withdrawal from him by Thelma and Zoe. I think they probably felt quite angry with him, and some of Thelma's anger was displaced on to the visitor blocking the television, whilst some anger was given expression by the domestic. Graham's feelings by the end of that observation show the sense of futility and rejection that many of the patients feel as a result of being institutionalised: feelings stirred up by the abandonment in Graham's holiday and final leaving, which were then evacuated into him when he returned.

Graham's departure hurt because, as I reminded him, he would be sorely missed. I felt Thelma's dream was an unconscious gift and acknowledgement of her appreciation of Graham's interest. The dream conveyed something of how reduced she felt, like the tennis ball. Her life on the ward was not the game she'd expected; little was left in her life, and she felt the loss. In the penultimate observation Graham found the leaving difficult and, like the patients, he tended to withdraw into sleepiness.

At the final observation Thelma's absence indicates the painfulness of the good-byes for these elderly patients, because I think she found it too hard to be there to say good-bye. Zoe's not sitting with Graham seemed to express the feeling of despair about making contact when faced with more loss. I thought Graham's brief contact and departure was a painful reminder of the many previous losses in the patients' lives and of current losses in the absences of the staff on the constantly changing shift system and because of holidays and illnesses. It was also a reminder of the deaths of fellow patients, sometimes after only a very brief time on the ward. The staff's sarcasm as Graham left seemed to express their anger about being left with these patients, and having to manage their patients' endless grief.

I think it very important that carers give notice about their absences to their elderly patients to give them time to work through some of the feelings which are stirred up and to help the carers understand more about their patients feelings. But it is a painful process. Before Graham began the observations I had encouraged him from the start to tell staff and patients about his holiday and finishing dates and to keep these two endings in mind. Later, he admitted he had thought this concern of mine about endings was just a 'bee in my bonnet'. I think in the final observations, before and particularly after his holiday, Graham began to feel the sting of the feelings about loss which the patients suffered.

Graham and I learned a great deal from Thelma and Zoe, and later the nil-by-mouth lady, Iris, as I think they spoke on behalf of all the patients. They showed us something of the anguish of trying to continue an 'ordinary' life on these long-stay wards when so much has gone and when faced with so many endings and good-byes; it is so painful that many prefer to withdraw into passivity and mutism. I would like to conclude by quoting part of a poem which Valerie Sinason wrote of Maureen, one of her handicapped patients:

There is only so much anyone can take
with an eye and an ear, no words
and a broken brain

There are only so many leavings
with no working legs and a
damaged heart.

(1992, p. 254)

8

WORKING WITH KEYWORKERS OF ELDERLY PATIENTS

Introduction

Shortly after starting at the hospital a few of the long-stay patients were referred to me by the consultant physician or the care group manager. I proposed taking up the referrals by working with the patients' keyworkers as a form of some in-service support and training for the keyworking system. The keyworker was the member of care staff designated as responsible for a particular patient, particularly for getting to know the patient and for working with the patient whenever the staff member was on duty. My proposal to work with the keyworkers was welcomed by management and staff. I saw the task as thinking with the keyworker about their patient's emotional experience of being in long-stay care. I aimed to offer support to the keyworkers by giving some space for them to talk about their own feelings and by helping them understand that some of the feelings they experienced could be unconscious communications from their patients.

An unexpected outcome of this work was that quite soon keyworkers brought some instances of abusive treatment of their patients. Although examples of abuse of the elderly in institutions have been well documented in this country, there has been little systematic research into it. Most of the research into 'elder abuse' has been done in America and Canada, in domestic or family care, but there has been difficulty reaching agreement about definitions of abuse and methodologies (Glendenning, 1993). What has become clear is the importance of the care-giving relationship, because it is recognised that abuse, whether in an institutional or domestic setting, 'exists within the context of a relationship and represents a care-giving relationship gone awry' (Phillips, quoted by Nolan, 1993, p. 150). A recent contribution to thinking about the prevention of abuse has emphasised the need to understand more about the care-giving relationship, particularly to see it as a dynamic and changing relationship. It is important to recognise that it is not simply concerned with the physical care of the elderly, but involves emotional needs for elderly patient and carer. It is important too to appreciate that in the care-giving role, as well as stresses, there are rewards and satisfactions (Nolan, 1993). I believe the work reported here is a contribution to understanding more about the care-giving relationship, whether in institutions or domestic settings, not only in bringing instances of abuse to light, but also in working preventatively by exploring the difficulties as well as the satisfactions in the work.

Much of what I did in this work could be offered by an experienced and possibly more senior colleague to carers, whether carers are staff or family. Carers have to bear the physical and emotional strain of close contact with ill and damaged and sometimes angry and provocative patients. I simply took a professional interest in the carers' work and encouraged them to think about their patients' feelings by following my example and imaginatively putting themselves in their patient's shoes. I tried to help them understand how it felt to be that patient in long-stay care. This work was challenging a defensive process in the institution in which staff often split off and denied a capacity to think about their patients' feelings, in order to protect themselves from the distress of empathising with their patients' emotional pain; and perhaps in order to protect the institution from the thoughts and feelings they would otherwise have experienced (A. Dartington, 1994). As I indicated earlier in Chapter 2, because of my role as the psychologist, the capacity to think about patients' feelings became located in me in the institution. By working with the keyworkers, I aimed to repair the split by showing them that, with support, it was possible to bear to think and feel with their patients. Though thinking in this way made the work more stressful, I felt ultimately it could be more satisfying. The work also illustrates the danger that when staff have no opportunity to talk about and understand their own feelings or their patients', then not thinking can easily lead to retaliatory and abusive practices.

The staff referred to the patients and each other by first names. I usually addressed the patients by their surnames, because I did not agree with the quick intimacy that immediate use of first names implies, particularly for patients from a generation used to formality. However, in the discussions with the keyworkers and in the following accounts, I adopted their convention and refer to staff and patients by first names.

A struggle between recovery and despair: Barbara and Mrs Dulcie May

Note how this work meant keeping in mind Barbara's and her patient's hope and despair. Note how showing Barbara some meaning in her patient's behaviour enabled her to make connections with her experience of the patient and with her own experience of ageing.

Barbara is an enrolled nurse who has worked for many years in the hospital. Most recently she had been on the rehabilitation ward before being transferred to work again on one of the long-stay wards. She had been on the ward for several months when I started working with her. She is a vivacious woman in her late fifties, full of life and good humour. I used to meet her in the early evenings, sitting in the nurses' office looking out on to the ward. As I got to know Barbara I became impressed with her sensitivity to her elderly patients. A touching tribute came from one of her patients, an Indian woman, who spoke no English, when she pointed to Barbara and said to her grandson 'She loves me!'

I was asked to see Dulcie May, an 80-year-old woman who had been transferred from the rehabilitation ward to the long-stay ward following a car accident which resulted in her losing her speech and memory. A speech therapist visited her regularly and found she could sometimes communicate by writing. She could walk with some assistance and could do a few tasks for herself, but was generally incapacitated by the accident and in a great deal of distress.

Barbara was Dulcie's keyworker. She told me Dulcie had been hit by a car when crossing the road with her husband, who was uninjured. The husband suffered from dementia and Dulcie had been looking after him for several years. Following the accident her husband was admitted to a nursing home because there was no one else to look after him. Dulcie had been asked if she wanted to join her husband in the nursing home. She seemed adamant against doing so and instead wanted to live with her brother. Barbara told me Dulcie was beginning to recover her memory, but then kept forgetting where she was. Apparently she had been actively involved in the local community and used to go out each day to various luncheons. Barbara was full of admiration for the way she struggled to speak and to remember. Barbara said Dulcie used to cry whenever any of her visitors left her and recently she had screamed at lunchtime on the activities ward. I talked to Barbara about Dulcie's shock and pain at awakening to her disabled state; instead of being at a social luncheon, she found herself surrounded by disabled elderly patients.

The following week when I saw Barbara she told me Dulcie had written that she was lonely. But when they took her to the dayroom, after briefly acknowledging the other patients, she wanted to be taken back to her bed. I said I thought it was unbearable to be reminded of her disabled state by seeing other patients who were like a reflection of herself. Barbara said she had a similar thought when she noticed Dulcie preferred being with the staff. She went on to say that Dulcie seemed only to want to live in the present; she mostly wrote 'hungry' asking for food, or 'tired' when she wanted to be put to bed. It was unclear whether she had any memory for the accident. She showed little interest in the past or future. I said I felt the accident had been a brush with death, and a lively and vigorous woman had been confronted with her ageing and vulnerability. Barbara blushed as she recalled an incident with her own adolescent son when he objected to the clothes she was wearing, saying she looked like a teenager. She had been angry with him, but in telling me she poignantly saw difficulties in facing her own ageing.

We talked some more about Dulcie's distress about her age catching up with her. Barbara said she usually found that it was more difficult for the male patients to accept what had happened to them. I recalled that Dulcie had been the head of the household for some years, caring for an increasingly dependent husband. Because of his dementia he had little memory and now she felt like him and only had a present. I thought the disability around her would remind her of her husband's incapacities and her fears for him and herself.

The next week Dulcie seemed to be speaking more. She was more lively and had been going to the activities ward. She'd conveyed to

Barbara that her family hadn't wanted her to marry her husband; there was some feeling he wasn't good enough for her. It seemed even now her family were objecting to her going to live with him at the nursing home. But her husband was regularly brought to see her. Sometimes he seemed not to recognise her, though when it was time for him to leave they both cried.

Two weeks later, Dulcie had become withdrawn and depressed again. Barbara said she only spoke when spoken to and only looked forward to going to bed. Barbara was keen to move her to the more stimulating environment of a nursing home. I said I felt Dulcie was probably despairing because as she made some progress she would also realise that, however much she improved, she would never be the same as before. I thought Dulcie might feel life wasn't worth living any more. Barbara said one of the doctors had suggested Dulcie might be able to return home, but she thought that most unlikely. I said it was difficult to hold on to the hope and the sadness, without exaggerating what might be possible and without being overwhelmed by despair. Then Barbara said she found it difficult to talk to Dulcie and Dulcie didn't seem to want to talk about her past. I said it was important to talk to Dulcie about her present disappointments and fears about the future, in the wake of her disabilities. Barbara replied that everything was getting her down and she talked about problems with other staff on the ward. She had tried to introduce various changes in the keyworker system, but she felt the staff were jealous of her and there was rivalry about who could do the various jobs on the ward. I said the rivalry amongst the staff avoided facing their despair about what couldn't be done for these very ill and damaged patients and avoided taking in the patients' despair about what they could no longer do for themselves.

For the next few weeks there was some excitement as Dulcie continued to make progress. She regained a good deal of her former capacities, her memory recovered and she was able to speak again, though she remained frail and in need of supervised care. There was a struggle between members of Dulcie's family, herself and Barbara about whether she would go to live in the nursing home with her husband, go to a separate nursing home or remain as a long-stay patient on the ward. Barbara was keen for her to be reunited with her husband. I said that perhaps they didn't want to be with one another; they might be glad to live separately. Barbara seemed to have a view of them walking off hand in hand into the sunset. Barbara laughed as I said this. She was deeply shocked to see how strongly she felt that they should be together and how this had prevented her from discovering just what it was that Dulcie wanted.

Two months later Dulcie and her husband were given a trial period of living together at the nursing home. In the time leading up to the move, Barbara was then careful to keep more detached from Dulcie and was less insistent that this trial period should succeed. As it happened it was successful and they stayed together in the nursing home.

Commentary

My taking up the referrals like Dulcie, by working with the key-workers, was soon accepted by the staff at the hospital. I think this was because it was seen to be helpful. Barbara was generous in telling other staff about her appreciation, saying the work had a beneficial impact on her thinking and she felt more aware of her patient's feelings. Perhaps it was the meetings in the early evenings, but sometimes I thought of my role in relation to Barbara, like a husband who comes home and hears about the day's troubles – particularly problems with the children – and thereby offers some support by thinking about his wife's worries. I felt I was able to help Barbara make some sense of Dulcie's behaviour, like the screaming and her reluctance to mix with the other patients, and help Barbara understand that feelings stirred in her could be a communication of how her patient felt. It seemed especially important to help Barbara keep in mind Dulcie's grief and resist the urge to provide an exciting environment in which there would be no space for sad feelings. At the same time, the hope that Dulcie could recover needed acknowledging, together with the disappointment that she would not recover as everyone wished. These attitudes seemed quite split, sometimes being expressed in exaggerated ways in different staff, like the doctor's hope that Dulcie would be able to return home alongside Barbara's feeling of despair. The argument about whether Dulcie should live with her husband in a nursing home included a similar split, as though if she did not go to live with him she would not be contaminated by any disability, his or hers, or that if she did they could be reunited as a wholesome, happy couple. I aimed to help Barbara achieve a more realistic view of Dulcie's future and to be less driven to impose her own happy ending on a tragedy. I felt if she could help Dulcie grieve for what had happened then perhaps Dulcie would be able to make the most of what remained of her life.

Working with a persecuting grief:
Melody and Mrs Ruth Scott

Note in this work that when it was possible to think about the patient's feelings of grief and loss and to give space for some of the keyworker's personal bereavement, the keyworker did not feel so persecuted by her patient's feelings. There was then some opportunity for sad and appreciative feelings to be shared between the keyworker and her patient.

Melody is an Afro-Caribbean staff nurse in her late twenties. She worked on the same ward as Barbara who suggested she see me about Melody's patient, Ruth Scott. Melody told me Ruth was 89 years old. She had married for the first time when she was 72 and then five years ago she had become ill with Parkinson's Disease. Her husband had looked after her until he died, five months ago, when she was admitted to hospital. She had been on this ward for the last two months.

Melody said she kept feeling irritated with Ruth because she was always making a strange 'mewing' noise. Melody asked me 'Why does she do that?' I could see she felt quite tormented by the mewing. When I asked her to describe the mewing, she mewed like Ruth and it made me think of a cat's miaow. So I said maybe Ruth was calling for her cat. Perhaps, along with so much that she had lost, including a husband whom she had married so late in life, she had also lost her cat. Melody softened as she heard these comments. More sympathetically she told me how Ruth often cried, curled up in bed and withdrew into herself. Sometimes she mentioned having dreams to Melody but she did not say what she dreamt of. I said perhaps she dreamt of all that she missed; I felt she was consumed with grief. Melody looked sad and told me of her uncle who had recently died.

The next week Melody greeted me with obvious pleasure, immediately telling me indeed Ruth had had a cat! Melody had asked her about her life and her husband. Ruth told Melody her husband's name, but she seemed puzzled by Melody's interest and said 'What's it got to do with you?' But Ruth had gone to bingo during the week and seemed to have enjoyed it. Melody was pleased. I felt Melody wanted Ruth to be active and enjoy herself and I reminded her that Ruth needed some space to grieve for all that she had lost.

She then asked me what other information she could find out about Ruth. I encouraged her to simply see what Ruth wanted to talk about, just to follow her conversation and perhaps tell her a bit about herself and her own life. Again Melody asked me, 'Why does Ruth mew, then?' I said I thought she was calling to her lost cat, her lost husband and perhaps even the children she never had.

During the next two weeks Melody told me that Ruth called out in a distressed state much of the time. I said she might feel in a panic that everyone would disappear from her life, as she could feel she herself might die at any time. I suggested that Melody reminded her of a daughter and granddaughter she never had and who would in all probability have looked after her now. Melody said she'd asked her about children and Ruth told her how much she'd have liked to have had a daughter. Melody looked sad as she told me this.

Two weeks later, Melody said that Ruth was constantly calling out 'Help, help!', and they couldn't discover what it was she wanted or what frightened her. She had spoken to Melody about having 'regrets' but did not say more, except a confusing comment that she had 'impersonated someone'. In a quieter moment she said she liked the red T-shirt Melody wore, it was her favourite colour. I said I thought she was telling Melody how she appreciated her loving care which reminded her of other good experiences in her life. Ruth had mentioned her mother and again a sense of regret, but would say no more to Melody. Then Melody remarked how different Ruth was now, because she was talking more to her. Melody said she was to be away for the next few weeks and I encouraged her to tell Ruth and say for how long she'd be away and when she'd be back. I reminded Melody how important she was to Ruth, especially now that Ruth had begun talking. It was probably a huge relief to talk, because it would be so awful to die with a lot of bad stuff inside her head. Several weeks later Ruth died and I had a final meeting with Melody to talk about her feelings in losing this patient.

Commentary

I felt that Ruth was grief-stricken and probably felt persecuted by her losses, especially the loss of a husband from a late marriage. It seemed some of this state of mind had been conveyed to Melody who felt tormented by the mewing and unable to think about its meaning, which may also have captured some of Ruth's difficulty of finding a meaning in her own life. Melody was clearly relieved to have some understanding of Ruth's behaviour.

I had a reciprocal difficulty in understanding Melody because of her accent. Sometimes I could not understand her even after I'd asked her to repeat herself several times. As I think about this now, she was perhaps vividly conveying to me her frustration with not being able to make sense of her patient. I wonder, too, if Ruth had difficulty in understanding Melody and how Ruth, who was white, felt about having a black nurse caring for her. But these were not questions I felt I could put to Melody because of my own difficulty in addressing the meaning of race and difference in this work. In retrospect, I wish I had been able to tackle these questions head on, because not doing so was disabling to Melody by treating her as if she was not up to considering these issues with me.

Melody may have wished to distance herself from being in emotional contact with Ruth's grieving, especially because Melody was carrying her own bereaved feelings for her uncle. As with Barbara, there was an intolerance of sad feelings and a wish to to urge the patient into activities such as the bingo sessions. When I showed I could bear to think of Ruth's misery, so Melody began to do so too. She recalled more of Ruth's distress and could feel sad for her, which put her in touch with her own sad feelings. When there could be some understanding it seemed to lead to some good contact between them (for example, in the compliments about the red T-shirt). At that time I think Ruth felt more in touch with good internal and external objects and less consumed by destructive feelings.

Working with an aggressive patient and abuse on the ward: Betty and Mr Arthur Green

Note how thinking with the keyworker about the patient's grief challenged some of the negative assumptions about him and enabled her to challenge unthinking and abusive treatment on the ward.

Betty had trained as an enrolled nurse but had not pursued nursing. Many years later, she came to work in the hospital as an untrained care assistant. She is a somewhat bluff character, a rough-cut diamond, warm and intuitive. When one of her patients was referred to me she was interested and pleased to work with me. Usually I talked to her in the office on the ward. Once she came to my office, though she seemed to feel guilty about taking time off from the ward to see me. She said she felt she should be working, and I said 'But this *is* working!'

Arthur Green was an 80-year-old patient admitted into long-stay care just a few weeks before Christmas. Shortly after his admission he was referred to me because he had hit some of the care assistants on the ward. He suffered from Parkinson's Disease and cancer.

My first meeting with Betty was the week before Christmas. Betty described Arthur as a 'bag of bones'. She said he tended to sit for most of the day with his eyes closed, except when she went to him. She used to joke with him and ask 'Are you in or are you out?' Usually he would open his eyes and answer 'In!' Betty said Arthur could also be verbally abusive. At that time he was the only male patient on the ward. But she said Arthur had not punched her and that she gave him 'as good as he gets', meaning she swore back at him when he swore at her. She discovered that he had a sweet tooth and quickly calmed down if she gave him a lolly or a cake. More sympathetically, she said he had been 'dumped' on the ward, with little preparation and no choice about whether he wanted to be there. His wife had been looking after him at home but was now no longer able to manage. Betty was concerned about his wife because she looked thin and undernourished, so she and the other staff always encouraged her to have some lunch with Arthur when she visited. One of the staff who had been hit complained that Arthur was like her violent husband. Betty and the staff believed Arthur had always been a violent man, but they were surprised his wife visited regularly and seemed so close to him. I said I thought Arthur was bitter about what had happened to him and terribly angry. I encouraged her to find out more about him.

Following a two-week Christmas break I saw Betty again, this time in my office. She had spoken with Arthur's daughter who told Betty that her father had only become violent late in life, after the onset of his illnesses. Previously he had been a kind, loving father and husband. As we talked Betty began to understand Arthur's violence as an expression of his anger about his illnesses and the incapacitating effects, and the loss of his independence and now the loss of his home and family life. Then Betty told me she was unhappy about the way Arthur was being treated on the ward. Because of his violent outbursts he was separated from other patients, who were in the day-room. He was left in a chair alongside his bed at the other end of the ward, in a draught. I talked to Betty about the cruelty in this way of treating him. She thought they could place Arthur in the day-room out of striking distance from other patients, so that at least he could be with the others and watch television. I suggested Betty talk to her colleagues on the ward, try to explain how Arthur felt and why he might be violent.

The next week Betty reported that Arthur had been taken to the day-room. When some staff objected, apparently she said: "Well, Paul Terry said 'Why not give it a try?''' Betty was still worried about him and I agreed to have a meeting with her and Arthur together. She took me to him to arrange it. I found a shrunken, emaciated man, hunched in an armchair, his eyes closed. There seemed to be some secretion around his eyes and Betty explained that he was suffering from an eye infection. But when I introduced myself he managed to open his eyes, looked pleased about a meeting and checked he had correctly understood the appointment time and day.

The day of the meeting Arthur's wife was visiting, so I suggested she join us. She took over the meeting, insisting, in a nervous and guilty way, that Arthur tell us how happy he was here, how good the staff were to him and how impossible it had been for her to manage. Arthur complied and agreed with what his wife said, but he would not agree that he was happy. As his wife talked on he gradually withdrew and eventually fell asleep. Just before we were due to finish he woke and warmly shook my hand as we arranged to meet again. Because of Betty's change of shifts and some holidays it was not possible for me to meet with her and Arthur, so I met him on his own on two more occasions. At these meetings he was confused and even seemed to be hallucinating, scarcely in touch with me or his surroundings. His condition worsened and he died shortly after.

Commentary

I think Arthur's experience reflects some of the problems for elderly male patients on mostly female patient and staff wards, because of the intimate physical contact and the implicit sexuality. Male patients are sometimes explicitly sexually provocative, and not surprisingly female staff find it hard to think or talk about sexual feelings stirred by the work. The staff seemed to have a quite negative transference to Arthur. Leaving him alone in a draught was retaliatory and abusive. Betty could see a connection between her being able to be verbally angry with Arthur and him not punching her, as well perhaps as her not having to join in physically abusing him. When she could question the assumption that Arthur had always been violent, she could bring the abuse to our work and go back to the ward and challenge it. The way she quoted me, in statements I don't recall making, shows how important the relationship with me was in giving her support to address unthinking and abusive behaviour. In the meeting with Arthur's wife it is apparent how difficult it can be for relatives to think about a patient's unhappiness or treatment on the ward when the relatives can feel guilty about no longer looking after the patient and perhaps frightened, that if they dared to complain, the patient would be sent back home.

I occasionally saw the keyworkers and their patients together. I think in this instance I offered to see Arthur because I was concerned to give Betty as much support as possible while the other staff were hostile to Arthur. At these times I think I joined with the keyworker like a couple thinking about the helpless infantile state of their patient.

Valerie Sinason has written of very subtle forms of abuse that can occur, even between mother and baby. (Observing a mother and baby, in weekly visits over one or two years, is a usual part of training to be a psycho-analyst or a psycho-analytic psychotherapist.) For example she describes an observation of a mother bathing a young baby in which, when the mother first started wiping the baby's mouth, the baby showed signs of discomfort, which continued for some weeks though with less intensity. After just six weeks Sinason noticed the baby started smiling when the towel touched his mouth and the smiling continued. The mother and (for a while) Sinason too believed that the baby was enjoying this moment, though Sinason began to feel that the mother had some uncomfortable appreciation of the aggressiveness in her behaviour. Even at six months, when the baby briefly showed some distress at the mother wiping his mouth sharply, a week later he was smiling again. In the context of a care-giving relationship, I think Sinason's observation shows how abusive behaviour can be covered over, in quite collusive ways 'to avoid unwelcome realisations' (1988) of abuse by the carer or the one who is cared for.

Sinason also points out that how an infant is handled, in being dressed, undressed, cleaned or fed, 'can carry many disguised sadistic or erotic overtones'. So too with these elderly patients who, like infants, are also helpless and dependent and vulnerable to these subtle and not so subtle forms of abuse. Like Sinason's abused children, elderly patients can also feel they have to 'swallow' the abuse. For example, I heard of one carer who, prior to washing her patient, used to leave her stripped naked, cold and exposed, for quite unnecessary lengths of time. On another occasion I was told of staff feeding patients by hand whilst being busily engaged in conversations with each other, ignoring their patients.

One of Barbara's female patients for whom my help was sought, provoked the staff by smearing her faeces over her bed and surroundings. Barbara found it helpful when I gave some meaning to this repellent behaviour by comparing it to the protests prisoners had made in Northern Ireland. She said she'd never thought of the patients experiencing long-stay care like a prison but could see that the smearing had started when this patient had been told she would never return home. With this understanding Barbara was able to challenge abuse on the ward when she called a stop to staff barricading this patient with tables in one corner of the ward because of the smearing behaviour.

Anna Dartington (1994), from her consultation work, has drawn attention to the necessity of nurses having the opportunity to think about their feelings: for example, to understand their anger and hatred of patients who seem to refuse to get better and thus frustrate the staff's reparative drives. If staff have the opportunity to talk about their feelings, they are less likely to retaliate. Angry or provocative patients are vulnerable to retaliatory behaviour from carers, especially in view of the 'potential sadistic abuse of the absolute power that staff inevitably have over in-patients' (Dartington, 1994). Yet, as Dartington points out, the anxieties about having such power are rarely talked about. My work with Betty and Barbara shows that when there are opportunities to talk about their feelings about patients, staff can successfully challenge abusive practices on the wards.

Pursuing suspicions of physical abuse

Note, as I endeavoured to pursue the suspicions of abuse, how my feelings of shock, denial and anger created difficulties and how important it was to have access to a colleague to process some of these feelings in order to be able to think and take action.

Seven months after taking up my post at the hospital, I started working with a keyworker concerning a patient who was causing disturbance on the ward because he was constantly shouting day and night. He had suffered two strokes and could no longer speak, except for shouting expletives. It was also difficult to determine how much he could understand of what was said to him. In an early discussion with the keyworker, almost as an aside, she mentioned that she was worried about recent things which had happened to her patient. I asked what sort of things. She told me of blisters which had appeared on his thighs and of bruises on his shoulders, for which there was no explanation. There had been an incident when, as he was being undressed for a bath, his shoe had been taken off in such a rough manner that his toenail had been torn off. I felt stunned and left the interview in a troubled state of mind, having arranged to meet again with the keyworker the following week. I had to go on to other meetings elsewhere and it was only in the early evening, when I was about to leave the hospital, that I recalled the talk with the keyworker. I felt more and more uneasy, especially because I appeared to have simply forgotten about it and because I had left the matter quite unresolved. So, before going home, I called in on my senior colleague, the clinical psychology manager. It was a great relief to talk about what I had heard from the keyworker because I felt some of my own shock and horror was understood. I then felt more able to think with my colleague about what to do. We resolved that as soon as possible I would talk to the ward sister about the supected abuse and tell the keyworker what action I was taking.

When I met with the sister I found, on the one hand, she tended to have some kind of explanation for each of the incidents the key-worker had raised, while on the other hand she showed some anxiety although she implied that the source of abuse, if there were any, was outside her control. As the interview proceeded I began to feel that I must have imagined it and had got it all out of proportion. Afterwards I felt alarmed again and was unconvinced that much investigation or action would follow. I talked again with my senior colleague. We concluded I should prepare a letter to the hospital manager, with a copy to the ward sister, outlining the substance of what I had been told and my concerns.

I was aware of worrying about the effect this action would have on my work on the ward and in the rest of the hospital. I feared I would be seen as a whistle blower with damaging consequences for my work. I was also aware of feeling full of rage and indignation and wanting to punish those who had committed this outrage against a helpless old man. Most of all I was shocked about how I had myself been drawn into a state of disbelief and complacency.

The keyworker's worries were subsequently investigated by the hospital management. The worries were taken very seriously. No evidence of abuse was established. The keyworker said at first she was upset that I had taken this action, but later, when she discussed it with her partner, he agreed with my action and she realised she felt relieved. She had only recently completed her training and was fairly new to the hospital. I think she was probably ostracised for talking to me and not long after, to my regret, she left to take up a post in a different field of nursing. Much later I worked again with this patient, seeing him individually over several months until he died (see Chapter 5).

Commentary

A review of some of the recent literature on 'elder abuse' raises the difficulty of confronting abuse: 'How do I confront without sound evidence when all I have is a suspicion?' (Eastman, 1993). I think my experience of pursuing abuse shows that some of the difficulties are connected with the feelings which are provoked by the suspected abuse. The abuse may be so shocking and so unthinkable that there is a pressure to turn a blind eye and believe it could not happen. There is also the fear of retaliation and the fear of being retaliatory and abusive to the suspected abusers. My experience shows the importance of being able to consult with an independent and neutral colleague to get help in processing these feelings in order to think and take effective action.

9

SUPPORT GROUPS FOR CARE STAFF

Introduction

What are staff support groups?

There is little written about support groups, which is curious in view of the prevalence and popularity of support groups in various institutional settings. An article in the *British Journal of Psychotherapy* presents a detailed account of one session from a staff support group in a hospital setting, and three professionals give a 'clinical commentary' on the meeting. The professionals were a group analyst, a Kleinian psycho-analyst and an organisational consultant. There was general agreement amongst these professionals that a support group is not intended to be group therapy, but it has an educational aim in the sense of helping staff to understand more about their roles and the organisational constraints that can prevent them fulfilling the roles in a satisfactory and satisfying way. There was agreement, too, that understanding transference and counter-transference is useful for furthering organisational learning and promoting beneficial change. All three professionals stressed the importance of giving due weight to organisational constraints, such as understaffing as a result of cuts in services, which staff support groups are usually unable to influence. A useful warning is that there is often an underlying pressure to establish support groups as a way of locating institutional problems in the groups, encouraging a view that such problems are a result of personal failure on the part of staff (T. Dartington, 1993).

A chapter in a book called *The Unconscious at Work* distinguishes between sensitivity groups, staff dynamic groups and support groups. The authors point out that support groups are usually so called because of 'the hope of getting more support from colleagues, as well as from the consultant [who conducts the group], so as to cope better with painful aspects of the work' (Bolton and Zagier Roberts, 1994, p. 156). The authors emphasise the need to be alert to covert and unconscious aims of the groups which may throw the groups off course. They also warn against being drawn into a process in which the support group is 'making bearable what should not be borne' (p. 165).

In the work I shall report I see the *aim* of staff support groups as facilitating beneficial change by:

(a) helping the staff in their care role by offering a time and place in which there can be some thoughtful understanding of their emotional experience of working in the institution, in particular their experience of being in close contact with elderly frail patients;
(b) encouraging staff to think about their patients' feelings about being in long-stay care, showing the staff that some of their own feelings may be unconscious communications from their patients;
(c) helping staff understand how their feelings about developments and changes within the institution may affect their work;
(d) thinking about the relationship between the staff support group and the institution as a whole.

Background to the support groups

When I started at the hospital I was encouraged by the hospital manager to set up support groups for all the wards. I was able to accomplish this by offering fortnightly meetings of one hour for each ward. At first the support groups were held in a training centre away from the wards. Other staff were brought in to cover so that all staff on duty could attend. After six months the cover was withdrawn because of concern about the costs. The meetings then had to be held on the wards, in the staff office which overlooked the wards, sometimes without one or two staff who had to be on duty on the ward and often with interruptions from the phone and personal callers. There were usually four to six care staff present at each meeting, mostly all female staff because there were few male staff. As a result of the shift system, often only one or two of those present would have attended the previous meeting.

On all wards there was a common admission policy. Most patients were referred from the rehabilitation ward and were assessed by a 'long-stay panel' before being accepted into continuing care. The long-stay panel included management from the hospital, the consultant physicians and social workers. Once accepted the patients and their relatives were shown over the different wards in the hospital and invited to choose where they would like to go.

The staff were sometimes moved to different wards and there were different day and night staff. Only day staff attended the support groups. There were also 'agency' or 'bank' staff on all the wards to cover temporary absences, and sometimes they attended the support groups.

In this chapter I shall describe some of the meetings from a support group on a ward which I shall call the York ward.

The York Support Group

Introduction

I had started a support group for York staff from the second month after beginning at the hospital and continued for a year, until I began the weekly patient and staff meetings for three other wards (see Chapter 11). It was then not possible to continue the York group because of my limited time and the need to schedule the meetings in the early afternoon to accommodate the staff shifts. A few months after the group had ceased I had a request from the newly-appointed ward sister, Gloria, saying the staff wanted me to resume the group. Apparently a few of the staff had asked for the group again so she had posted up a list for all the staff to sign to see if enough staff were interested. A majority were in favour of the group being reinstated. As it happened one of the patient and staff meetings was to finish because its ward was closing, so I was able to start the York group again after a six-month gap. Two members of staff, Liz and Mavis, with whom I had worked on the ward that closed, were now in the York team and I had previously worked with Barbara and Melody individually in their role as keyworkers (as reported in Chapter 8).

I am going to describe some of the meetings over a period of six months from when I resumed the York group. During this time, perhaps typical of the turmoil now in the NHS, there were several major upheavals for the staff: in an effort to make necessary savings the health authority encouraged staff to apply for redundancy and early retirement; after several years' delay, plans to construct new buildings for the long-stay service were given the go-ahead; the management of the service was put out to tender for bids from the private sector; and the health authority was to merge with another authority to form a 'Trust'.

The first York Support Group Meetings following a six-month gap

Note how developments within the hospital led the staff to feel more and more identified with their elderly patients. Note the different ways staff tried to manage feelings of loss and rejection and how they tried to avoid sad feelings.

At the first meeting after resuming, the ward sister was angry with the other staff, complaining they had little to say even though they indicated they wanted the group. She complained, too, that the hospital manager said their ward should be more homely, like the other wards in the hospital. Gloria argued that individual homes are different, so why shouldn't the wards be different? She felt particularly criticised because the manager had said there was a lot of tension between staff on the ward. When I said she seemed to feel that the tension was her fault, she visibly softened in her demeanour and other staff started contributing. A young auxiliary, Fay, said she thought the tension was connected with the uncertainty about the future of the hospital, especially since the senior staff were leaving. (The care group manager and the senior nursing adviser, Diana, had both left within the previous two months.) Gloria agreed with Fay and with sadness she said that she couldn't go to Diana for support any more.

The following month Gloria looked glum and sat with her back to the other staff, staring out onto the ward. Melody spoke of the plans for the new buildings and the land on which they were to be built. She was worried that the buildings could not accommodate all the patients because they would be too small and there was too little land to build larger ones. Other staff joined in correcting this misperception, though they added their own misgivings. There was concern about how the patients would be allocated to the different sites. It was supposed they would probably go the site nearest to where their relatives lived, which would mean they would be dispersed. I said I thought the staff were also worried that the patients would die rather than move. They agreed, saying that they could tell who would die in the move. Two of the older nursing staff, Barbara and Liz, said that they felt the trained staff would no longer be wanted in the new buildings. They recalled other moves during the years in the hospital, sometimes with very short notice and little preparation. For example, Barbara described a whole ward being moved after having been told only a few days before.

A month later the staff had received a circular encouraging them to apply for redundancy or early retirement. There was an atmosphere of excitement as Barbara and Liz anticipated their early retirement. With a laugh I commented that it was like a leaving party! After a while the staff became subdued. One of the senior staff quoted a younger member of staff from another ward who had said that the older staff should go to make way for the younger staff. The older staff present were very angry. I said I thought the younger staff were doubtless worried about their future. Katie, a young auxiliary, agreed, saying she had a large debt she was paying off and was fearful about what she would do if she was out of a job. Rose, an older auxiliary, looked upset and told us her husband was now out of work and they had a mortgage to pay.

There was also some talk about the news that management of the service was to be put out to tender to the private sector. The staff were worried the private sector mainly managed part III accommodation (suitable for less dependent and more mobile patients) and had little knowledge of the type of care needed for the highly dependent patients in this long-stay hospital. Someone then mentioned that the ceiling on one of the other wards was said to be 'caving in'. I said that the service would cave in without them. They looked touched and sad. I asked why couldn't *they* organise a bid for the tender; after all, they knew about this service?

Commentary

The first meeting shows how feelings of criticism and failure can be passed down the institutional hierarchy. Staff in an elderly service are particularly susceptible to feelings of failure because of their helplessness to improve their patients' physical state or prevent them from dying. Moreover, the service as a whole was in great difficulty. The health authority was in a financial crisis and decisions had already been taken to make cuts in services which would have difficult consequences but, as Tim Dartington (1993) has pointed out, there is a danger that a support group can collude to maintain a view of the hospital as a caring system, in which such difficulties are only understood as personal failures.

In particular, the material shows how the ward sister, Gloria, who was consumed with feeling criticised, passed those feelings onto the junior staff when she attacked them for not speaking. In turn she had probably been the recipient of similar feelings from the hospital manager, who had lost her two senior colleagues, the care group manager and the nursing adviser. I think these departures felt rejecting and destabilising. The care group manager who left had been openly critical of his own manager.

Pointing out that Gloria felt personally responsible challenged her assumption that she was indeed responsible. She then seemed to feel less angry and allowed some space for the junior staff to talk about their feelings, particularly some sad feelings, about the events in the hospital. It is likely that Gloria's anger had been blocking the expression of the sad feelings.

The next meeting shows how a move to two new smaller buildings seemed to provoke infantile feelings of being small and abandoned, expressed in the anxieties about the buildings being too small and the patients not being accommodated. It was important to draw out the staff's worries about patients dying. It is well known that during such moves there is a high mortality rate of elderly patients. But staff often found it difficult to talk about their feelings about patients dying, especially because the staff were so frequently exposed to death. I think at this time it was more difficult for staff to talk about losing their patients because they were confronted with so many other losses. The staff generally felt unwanted by the health authority which threatened to abandon the service to the private sector. The older trained staff felt quite identified with their patients: they anticipated they would be rejected in favour of untrained carers. In addition, the move revived memories of other losses and moves.

The later material shows how the staff tried to manage the burden of these painful feelings. The excitement about the possible redundancy payments indicated an almost manic denial of feelings of rejection which soon gave way to a more persecutory split between the older and younger staff, in a quite primitive rejection of the old by the young. The group thus became flooded with feelings very closely resembling those of their elderly patients. The splitting between young and old staff seemed an attempt by the younger staff to rid themselves of these feelings. It reminds me of the practice in some cultures where the old who were ailing were ejected from their communities and left to die (de Beauvoir, 1970), which of course is not so different from the practice of admitting these elderly patients into a long-stay hospital. By my attending to some of the younger staff's fears, there was a reduction in the splitting, a 'caving in' of some of the persecutory defences against the worries and some space for sad and angry feelings. I felt it was important to acknowledge the valuable contribution of the staff because of their sense of being unvalued. I also thought it useful to challenge their sense of helplessness about the tendering.

Following an Easter holiday

Note the development in the meetings when staff felt some of their anxieties about the changes in the hospital were understood and they had an opportunity to work through some of these feelings: staff were then able to bring concerns about their patients and acknowledge satisfaction from the work.

When I met the staff a month later the meeting was unusually late in starting. I had come back with a haircut and there were jokes about my 'short hair'. Gloria was particularly angry and kept joining and then leaving the meeting, which made me angry. There seemed to be confusion and fear about the tendering, though the internal management was now putting in a bid. The staff complained about a new senior nurse, Marilyn, who was not present. She was described as throwing her weight around, treating the others as if they didn't know anything. I talked about the difficulty of the feelings of not knowing what was going to happen to the service and the problem of what to do with these feelings, and where to put them.

A month later the staff were in low spirits. They talked of recent thefts of some patients' money from the ward. There was suspicion that a member of staff was responsible and there was a tense atmosphere in the meeting. I said I felt they were very unhappy about what might be stolen from them, like their jobs, and now it seemed they would not even be entitled to redundancy or early retirement. (It looked like staff in the long-stay service would not after all be eligible for redundancy or early retirement because of the changes in the long-stay service.) Some of the staff sadly agreed, one saying there was 'nothing left' and that it was hard to continue working with all the uncertainty.

The next fortnight there was a moving discussion about difficult feelings whenever patients died. Two young auxiliaries talked of how a recent death on the ward reminded them of friends who had died. Rose, an older auxiliary, spoke of how very upset she had been about the death of one of her patients for whom she was the keyworker. The new staff nurse, Marilyn, who was present, seemed quite withdrawn. When I asked her what she thought about what had been said, she told us she was a born-again Christian and had no fears or upset about death.

A fortnight later the thieving was brought up again. I repeated what I thought the staff feared would be stolen from them in terms of redundancy payment or job security. Some money had been found on the ward and there was some confusion about whether it belonged to the patients or staff. I talked of the confusion resulting from the staff feeling so much like the patients when the staff faced so much loss themselves because of the move and possible change of management.

The next fortnight there was a lighter, more thoughtful atmosphere in the meeting. A young auxiliary, Vera, talked about one of her patients, George, for whom she was the keyworker. Vera felt she could not work with George and that he would be better with someone else as keyworker. He was slightly mobile and kept falling. Recently he had a bad fall and Vera took him to the casualty department for an X-ray. Apparently he kept calling her his wife and embarrassed her by making sexual overtures. I asked the staff to tell me what they knew about George. They all joined in with different bits of information.

George was suffering from Parkinson's Disease and dementia. He had been on the ward for a few months. His wife had breast cancer. His daughter had recently separated from her husband and she suffered from problems with alcohol. Some of the staff knew George's son, a handsome man who had been to the local grammar school. When the son turned up on the ward they thought he was an airline pilot in his uniform and then realised that he was 'merely a busdriver'.

I talked about the tragedies in George's life, his illnesses, his wife's cancer and perhaps his fear that she might die, as well as the likely ambitions and then disappointments he felt about his children. He suffered the additional pain that his wife had become a visitor in his life. In his confused state Vera probably seemed more like a wife to him since she spent so much time with him and looked after him in such an intimate way, like a wife would do. I said he probably felt quite frightened in Casualty, and perhaps he feared he was dying.

Some of the staff complained that George had been kept waiting for five hours at Casualty; it would have been less disturbing for him and everyone else if he had been seen more quickly. I reminded them of the chaos at the general hospital which was likely to merge with another hospital into a new 'Trust', the chaos in this hospital and how difficult it was to think under such conditions. They then talked about the uncertain future. The older staff still were hoping for early retirement, whereas the younger staff were feeling optimistic. Vera said she planned to take up nurse training in the Project 2000 scheme, and Katie said she hoped for a new job as a carer when the hospital moved. Again Marilyn looked withdrawn, but when I encouraged her to speak she said how much better the staff morale was here than in another hospital where she also worked part-time. She described a neglected work environment and a hostile and suspicious staff in the other hospital. She wondered if the better morale here was connected with these support meetings.

At the next meeting, George was discussed again. He was being taken to the general hospital to visit his wife who had been suddenly admitted, dying from cancer. A lot of concern was expressed about him. Vera said she was getting on better with him and had not pursued her request to change from being his keyworker. There was a delay in taking him to the general hospital because it was discovered he wasn't wearing his own trousers. He was upset and his trousers had gone missing. The two senior staff, Barbara and Liz, took the matter in hand, found the trousers and completed the arrangements for George to see his wife. They returned to the meeting expressing their pleasure about having sorted it out.

A fortnight later we had a final meeting before my summer holiday. Barbara and Liz had been to see the hospital manager about their future. Even though the Personnel Department had given them details of their likely redundancy payments, they were told they would not be able to take redundancy or early retirement because staff could not be released from the long-stay service. Union meetings had also been held about the possible consequences if staff were transferred to a private management. It seemed there could be no long-term guarantee that conditions of service or pensions would be protected. The staff were very angry. I said their hopes had been raised, only to be dashed.

There was a lot of worry about the tendering for the hospital which would not be decided for another two months. It was feared the tendering would be awarded to a private company. The staff exchanged worrying stories of their own and others' experiences of working for private nursing homes. In one home, where a former auxiliary was now working for less money, the patients were all taken out of bed at an early hour, kept waiting in their bedclothes and given a poor breakfast. Food and provisions for patients and staff were severely rationed there because of costs. The talk became more and more rapid, interspersed with a tense laughter, as I felt they struggled with feelings of anxiety and despair. I said I thought they felt unwanted and unvalued by the health authority which they felt intended to abandon them to a private management.

Commentary

The Easter holiday break galvanised feelings about loss in the group because in their transference to me the staff felt abandoned over the holiday. These feelings can be seen in the way the staff kept me waiting to start, as I had kept them waiting over the holiday and cut them short of the support groups, like, as they commented, my hair had been cut short. In my counter-transference about Gloria who kept coming and going, I experienced something of the staff anger with my coming and going. I did not interpret these transferential feelings because this would have encouraged a therapeutic dependency on me which would be inappropriate to a support group. Instead I saw my task as being to think about what light these counter-transference feelings could shed on how staff felt in their roles in the hospital.

The staff were especially vulnerable to angry feelings because of their grief about losses they anticipated in connection with changes in the hospital. If I had seen it then it would have been helpful to have talked about the anger with management who were abandoning them and threatening to cut them short of their pension and retirement benefits. However, the interpretation about their anger with Marilyn addressed some of the anger with management for leaving the staff in a great deal of uncertainty about the future. It was my hope too that this interpretation would ease their relationship with Marilyn from some of the feelings which seemed displaced onto her. It was especially important to help staff be more aware of their anger to avoid these feelings being expressed against the patients.

It was important that the discussion about the thefts, which was marked by suspicion and insinuation, did not turn into a witch hunt for the culprit. It was not the task of the support group to pursue the guilty party. The usefulness of interpreting the thefts in the context of developments in the hospital was that staff were thereby enabled to express more of their grief about the future. This work paved the way for the staff's grieving about recent deaths on the ward, a grief that these staff are always faced with. The material shows how staff not only experience the pain of losing their patients but have memories revived about their loved ones who have died. However, in the context of the group I think the born-again Christian position that Marilyn spoke of probably indicated there was also some split-off manic defence in the group against these sad, depressive feelings (see Chapter 1).

The further discussion of the thefts allowed the theme of loss for the staff to be worked through some more, and revealed another strand of meaning for the staff: how the losses and feelings of rejection they faced brought them much closer to their patients' grief with some resulting confusion. After I articulated this confusion with the patients, there were signs of relief and, significantly, at the next meeting there was the first substantial discussion about a patient since the group had resumed. Thus working through some of the grief about the institutional changes and some of the ensuing role confusion enabled the staff to get back into role and to think with concern about their patients. In a sense it was helping them to reinstate a helpful split to differentiate themselves from their patients.

It is interesting that George, the patient the staff brought for discussion, encapsulated some of their concerns because he had various painful losses and disappointments, as he faced the death of his wife and had suffered a fall and was kept waiting a long time to know if anything had been broken. The staff were also struggling to face the losses in the move to new buildings which would probably sever some of the staff and patient relationships. Like George, they suffered a fall in their expectations about redundancy and early retirement payments; they were kept waiting because it was still unknown whom would be allocated to which site and if there would be a new private management, which might mean futher losses. The coincidence of George's problems with their own probably con-tributed to the feeling that he was unmanageable, voiced by his keyworker. The opportunity to discuss their feelings about George helped the staff disentangle themselves from George and find a sense of satisfaction in their work with him. In the discussion about George the staff were still working on their issues of loss at the same time as working consciously on the problems connected with George. I think it was unnecessary to make such an interpretative link which could have implied that I thought they were only working on their own issues and that I disregarded their genuine reparative feelings for George.

I think the final meeting before the holiday, in which the staff were again consumed with anger and worry about the future, shows the difficulty they had in sustaining thoughtfulness about the patients when the support of the groups was about to be withdrawn because of my summer holiday and when they were assailed by fears about changes in the hospital. They were being abandoned by their health authority management and by my going on holiday.

10

WORKING WITH MANAGERS OF A LONG-STAY SERVICE

Introduction

When I arrived at the hospital I asked the manager if, because of the part-time nature of my work, I could have regular meetings with her to catch up on events in the hospital between my visits. She agreed to weekly meetings. As time went by she came to value these meetings as opportunities for herself to reflect on the management issues. The meetings had evolved into consultations. In my second year, when the manager was on holiday she asked me to see her new deputy manager, and later the deputy asked if she too could see me on a weekly basis. These meetings became an important part of my work and I came to see my task in this consultation role as essentially thinking and offering understanding about the anxieties, conscious and unconscious, which the manager and her deputy had to manage: the staff's, the patients', the relatives' and their own.

There were many worries at this time of massive change for the service. The period of consultation to management described in this chapter covers the time just prior to the announcement of the results of the tendering for the management of the service until the hospital was moved to new buildings six months later. The purchasers announced that the management of the long stay service was awarded to a private company which would take over at the same time as the staff and patients moved to the new buildings. All the staff, with the exception of myself and other paramedics, were to be transferred to the employment of the company. Staff would keep their employment rights for an unspecified period after the transfer. They could not keep their NHS pension schemes but had to take out a new pension arrangement with the company. Old and new patients retained their NHS non-fee-paying status.

It seems that this move to privatise the management of the long stay service for the elderly is likely to reflect the future of these services. I shall summarise the anxieties connected with the resulting loss and change which had to be managed in the transfer to the private sector, a move which was felt quite concretely because it coincided with the service being relocated in two new purpose-built 'nursing homes'.

First, I shall briefly describe some of concepts which were particularly relevant to elucidating the anxieties in the work with the managers. It may be recalled from my general exposition in Chapter 1 that *projective identification* refers to an unconscious process in which unwanted aspects of the self are split off and projected into others who are then identified with those aspects, and that this process often has an effect on those who receive the projections. In an institution projective identification by its members can occur on a massive scale and various sub-groups or certain individuals may unconsciously be selected to carry certain projections. Just why some individuals or groups are susceptible to these projections is probably connected with their readiness to feel and act in certain ways: for example, someone who has their own grievances with authority is more likely to receive projections of negative feelings about authorities. Often the hope in this projective process is that the projected feelings can be managed and understood by the recipients of the projections (see section on containment, Chapter 1). Because this is an unconscious process, those individuals or groups who are the recipients of projections will believe that the feelings are their own and, as William Halton writes, 'they unconsciously identify with the projected feelings', and 'the state of mind in which other people's feelings are experienced as one's own is called the *counter-transference*' (1994, p. 16).

During the consultations the managers often brought incidents about particular staff members who worried them. My approach to these discussions was to think with the manager about what the difficult staff member might unconsciously be enacting on behalf of other groups, or even all the staff in the institution, as a result of being recipients of projections. The discussions therefore offered an opportunity to think about what might be gleaned about the institutional issues. This was not to ignore the difficulty with the individual staff member but, as Obholzer and Zagier Roberts have pointed out:

Treated as a group process, the underlying problem, as well as the individual's, is addressed. To treat it as one person's mis-behaviour allows everyone else to continue disowning and projecting aspects of themselves into the targetted individual, and the process will continue unabated, to the cost of both the individual and the institution. (1994, p. 133).

At times the managers too were recipients of various projections, and sometimes in the consultations I became aware of carrying certain feelings which were part of the problem being discussed. I saw my task as drawing the managers' attention to the projective processes and attempting to make sense of the projected feelings. In this way I wanted to support the management role in processing the staff's feelings and in 'maintaining a position at the boundary between inside and outside' (Obholzer and Zagier Roberts, 1994, p. 137). I aimed to help the managers be clearer about what belonged to themselves, to other individuals, to groups and to the institution as a whole. For myself it meant taking up 'a listening position on the boundary between conscious and unconscious meanings' and working 'simultaneously with problems at both levels' (Halton, 1994, p. 12).

Thinking about these projections with the managers also aimed at challenging tendencies for splitting processes in the institution and a paranoid-schizoid culture of fragmentation, fear and suspicion, particularly between staff and management. My hope was that the work would enable the service to function in a depressive mode in which we could tolerate and work through more of the complex range of feelings stirred by the changes in the service.

Anxieties about loss and change

Note how the move to a private company aroused strong competitive feelings amongst staff, and much anger, confusion and uncertainty for staff, patients and relatives, all of which had to be managed by managers who were themselves experiencing those feelings.

Staff anxieties

During the tendering process and just before the results were announced, one of the senior staff, Gwen, a popular figure in the hospital, had told some of her colleagues about two dreams she had. There was much talk about the dreams amongst the staff and the dreams became widely known in the hospital, I think because the dreams expressed many of the staff's worries.

In the first dream Gwen had a lot of plucked chickens which she was trying to sell. A man came along and told Gwen the chickens were no good and she must put the feathers back on. She started doing this when the deputy manager of the hospital came along and reproached her for putting the chickens with their feathers on in the oven. She told Gwen that this was not maintaining standards! In the second dream Gwen was in a space ship with the staff from her ward. Her senior nurse told her some of the staff were playing up and would have to go, and at that she began pushing some of the staff off the ship into outer space.

The first dream brings forward the staff concern about the service being transferred to the private sector. When it was known that a private company had won the tendering some of the staff talked about being 'sold down the river'. Trying to sell the plucked chickens also expressed worries about joining the commercial sector with a profit motive and maintaining the NHS standards. There was a great deal of suspicion about what interest a private company could have in looking after old people and fears that this move paved the way for the service to be made into a means-tested and fee-paying one. The patients were like the chickens plucked of so many aspects of their former lives, suffering horrendous loss. But now the staff were also like the chickens, plucked of their NHS pensions – the feathers for their nests in retirement – and perhaps also plucked of their beliefs that one day the state might provide this service for them in their old age as a right, not according to what they might afford. The impossibility of putting the feathers back on the chickens reveals the knowledge in the dream that in this process of change there was no going back.

The plucked chickens also resonated with staff worries about stories of colleagues working in the private sector, of services being run on very reduced resources with damaging effects on patients and staff. During this time the manager discovered one of the wards had taken to hoarding provisions which was against hospital policy, but which I felt demonstrated some of the unconscious fears about the future.

Interestingly in the dream it was the deputy manager who pointed out that standards were not being maintained. Although it is an appropriate part of the management role to try to maintain standards, it also reflected a tendency for senior staff to feel distrustful of junior colleagues: a process in which incompetence could be projected down the hierarchy and senior staff could feel more competent and more assured of a place in the future service. This aspect of the dream also echoed a split in which the deputy was sometimes seen in a negative and critical way, in contrast to the manager who needed to be preserved as a good and benign figure who would protect the staff in the changed private management.

The second dream vividly conveys the fears of being ejected from the new 'space ship' service. There seemed a belief, despite assurances to the contrary, that only selected staff would be retained in the new service. The suspicion seemed to be that this selection would be done on the basis of the management's favourites. Other assumptions about the way this selection might be done were enacted in conflicts between the staff. As reported earlier in the staff support group (Chapter 9), one young staff member said that older staff should leave to make way for the younger staff. During this time there were further instances of conflict between older and younger staff members and with some of the staff from racial minorities. The hospital manager was herself from a racial minority, but there was little direct conflict with her. It seemed strenuous efforts were being made to keep her as a benign authority.

There was excitement in the discussions about the dreams which reflected staff and management excitement about some of the changes ahead. Although there were worries about the new buildings, staff looked forward to working in a new purpose-built environment in which the patients would have the privacy of their own rooms.

Management anxieties

The managers shared many of the staff's fears for their own future and the future of the service. At one of my meetings with the manager and her deputy they discussed a staff group in which the staff had angrily complained about their ward manager, who was not present. The staff were angry because she had withheld news from an elderly patient whose son had died from AIDS. When the manager and her deputy discussed this with me they expressed anger with their own senior managers for being critical and unsupportive of them. This vignette captured a central difficulty for the managers in handling the staff anger and fears about what management was withholding from them, when at the same time the managers had to manage their own angry feelings. They were particularly vulnerable to being drawn into conflicts with staff in which they were often left feeling angry. Some of the anger the managers felt belonged to the staff, because fears about the future made it difficult for the staff to express their anger directly. In essence, because of worries about retaining their jobs, it was hard for staff to speak their minds, so they easily ended up too frightened to express their thoughts and feelings.

Staff anger about all the changes in the service remained a constant source of worry for the managers before and after the privatisation. From my own discussions with an organisational consultant/supervisor, I came to understand that the underlying worry was that if the anger went unexpressed then it would be the patients who would suffer, because they would be most vulnerable to the staff acting out, consciously or unconsciously, angry feelings. The managers also worried about being too harsh with the staff because of their own anger: for example, in taking disciplinary action. Patients who had their own grievances were also vulnerable to expressing anger on behalf of the staff. During the period of the move to new buildings and the transfer to private management there was an escalation in staff complaints about angry patients who shouted abuse and sometimes struck out at the staff. As a result of my work, the managers became attuned to the projective processes operating between staff and patients. At one meeting to discuss staff complaints about a patient, a manager introduced the discussion by saying she didn't want to hear about the patient, she wanted to hear about the staff feelings about the changes in the service. There followed a tirade of complaints. At another meeting, a case discussion of a patient who often shouted insults at the staff, a manager said she thought the patient was doing what the staff would like to do to the management.

Despite their impressive understanding of the staff's feelings, the managers at times became impatient with the staff's prolonged grieving: the sense of despair and hopelessness, sadness and fearfulness. There was also fragmentation in the service: the managers were called upon to deal with much splitting, reflecting the increase in the anxiety. For example, as the move took place the two new nursing homes were split, one being seen in an idealised way and the other as having all the problems of settling in. Within the home that was seen to be successfully settling, one-half of it was presenting recurrent problems with staff and patients whilst the other half seemed problem-free. In this home there were also tensions between a nursing model of care and what was described as a 'social model'. As time passed it became clearer that the major split which had to be managed was that between the values and standards of care of the NHS and those of the private company. There seemed a general belief amongst staff that, whatever the management of the private company said, their underlying interest was in saving money, particularly on staffing costs. Sometimes the managers seemed to enact the role of what was imagined to be a cost-conscious private manager.

The worries about costs were accompanied by guilt about some of the wastage in the NHS, as though private companies did not have wastage. There was much thought about where savings could reasonably be made without sacrificing the quality of care to the patients. There was also some hope that a new private management could renegotiate some services which previously had not been in the best interests of the patients. For example, the former catering arrangements had meant that breakfast had to be served at a very early hour to the patients, whereas flexible arrangements were more appropriate for these patients.

Patients' and relatives' anxieties

It was not at all clear what impact the transfer to a private company had for the patients, especially because it coincided with the move to new buildings. There was also a lobby by staff and relatives that the changes in the service should not be discussed with the patients because it would be too upsetting. Few patients were brought to the various meetings about the transfer and few expressed a view about it. From the more informal contact it seemed that the patients' worries, like the relatives', tended to focus on the design of the new buildings, especially on the fact that the patients would be mainly housed in single bedrooms. The worries were that the patients would miss the corridor-style wards where at least they could see and be seen, and that in the new single bedrooms they would be lonely and vulnerable because of the isolation. It seemed that the single bedrooms galvanised the staff's, patients' and relatives' sense of abandonment by the NHS and their consequent fears and vulnerabilities. Later, when the patients were moved into the new buildings, some of the patients expressed a worry that they would have to pay for their care.

Although meetings were held with representatives of the purchasers and the relatives, it seemed difficult for the relatives to take an active role in relation to the negotiations about the transfer. A few relatives were vocal about their worries, about maintaining the quality of care for their patients and about the financial aspects of the private company. An 'action group' was established to represent the relatives, but it was hard to recruit relatives for it. I felt that the relatives seemed to think the patients were no longer their responsibility; it was up to the purchasers and the staff to sort things out. Perhaps they were too frightened to make a fuss for fear that if they did so they might have to take over looking after the patients again, or pay for their care.

Commentary

Anton Obholzer has described the NHS as a 'keep-death-at-bay service' (1994, p. 171) because for our society the service is a social system used as a defence against anxieties about death. Following this view it is not surprising that long stay care for the elderly should have been one of the first of the NHS services to be transferred to the private sector, because these elderly patients confront us with helplessness to prevent physical and mental deterioration and death. There has been little public outcry either about the reduction in long stay care beds or the transfer to private management. It is as though by splitting off the care from the NHS, old age and death can be kept 'out of sight and out of mind'. The move of the long stay hospital to the private company and to the two new buildings was accompanied by a change of name because the new buildings were to be called 'nursing homes'. The name change seems intended to soften the severity of the patients' illnesses and their nearness to death.

I think it interesting that Gwen's dreams and the implicit interest in the unconscious had by this time become part of the culture of the hospital. I had not previously had dreams brought to the consultations with the managers. It can't be without significance that at that time I was becoming interested in Gordon Lawrence's pioneering work on 'social dreams' which can be part of consultation work. Lawrence describes images in dreams as 'two way in that they have something to say not only about the unresolved challenges facing the individual but also about the society in which the individual is located and conducts life' (1991, p. 290). In this latter sense Gwen's two dreams have something to say about the life in the hospital, though again, as Lawrence says:

> The discovery of the social meanings is never easy. What may be more important than the 'product' of the dream, the meanings, which can never be absolute, is the 'process' of arriving at the

range of meanings possible. It is this act of creativity that is the hallmark of Social Dreaming . . . It is a process which encourages the reflective nature of human beings as they try to make sense of their experiences in both their social and inner worlds. (p. 291)

Gwen's dreams illustrate the upsurge of competitive feelings provoked by the move to a private company and the resultant anxiety. In some respects the move reflected other changes in the NHS: in general the introduction of market-led forces, and in particular the purchaser/provider split within the service. But, as William Halton has pointed out, these changes lead to a clash between the traditional dependency culture of the health service and the culture of the market. He explains: 'In the dependency culture there is a primary concern for the welfare of the person in the dependent position, which has been an inspirational element in the work of teachers, health practitioners and others. As well as earning a living, the vocational element offered a channel for altruism' (1995, p. 188); whereas 'The primary value of the market is to maximize one's own advantage at the expense of others. Market transactions are transactions between rivals' (pp. 188–9). He concludes: 'Health and education have become chronically entangled with two contradictory value systems, with the structure and values of the internal market at variance with the dependency values required for client work. This acts as a source of confusion and stress, neither system being fully operative' (p. 191). In the consultations it was necessary to help the managers sort through the clash between the dependency culture of the NHS service and the competitive culture of the private company, to be clear about the primary task in the new organisation and their roles in facilitating the task. As I worked on this with them it became clearer that part of their task had become that of preserving the values of the previous NHS-based work within the new culture of the private company.

Following the move to the private company, as well as the increase in anxiety which Halton calls 'survival anxiety', there was much anxiety about change. I think the story from the two managers about the staff discussion of the young man who died from AIDS shows some of the underlying anxieties associated with change. Rosemary Gordon writes, 'Inevitably, the acceptance of change includes acceptance of death, the ultimate and inevitable change' (1978, p. 16). The staff's efforts to manage their anxieties led to much of the splitting between different staff: young-old, black-white, one nursing home and the other, and between the manager and her deputy. There was a frantic effort for some groups to survive as 'good' in contrast to others who were 'bad'. I believe this splitting was especially intense in the staff because the changes brought the staff closer to their patients' experiences of frightful loss. The splitting was an attempt to protect staff from the terror of feeling like their patients.

The AIDS vignette also illustrates the managers' double task of having to manage their own and the staff's anger about the changes, as well as the grief underlying some of the anger. That is to say much of the anger was of course justified, particularly about the way the changes had been brought in with little staff consultation. But some of the anger also operated as a block against grieving for the losses. This blocking anger mirrored anger staff had to face in some of their patients whose anger also avoided grieving. It was particularly difficult for the staff to mourn the losses because they were immersed in so much grief: their own grief about the changes and the patients' endless grieving for all their losses. Working with the managers it was necessary to keep the justified and blocking aspects of the anger in mind, to help them help staff get in touch with their sad feelings as well as their appropriate rage.

Working with the managers it was important to remember that they and their own managers, who had been superseded by the private company, had been powerless to prevent the move. In this sense of powerlessness the managers and the staff were again brought painfully closer to their patients who were helpless. Thus the danger for the managers was in trying to rid themselves of these feelings by taking it out on others, making their staff feel powerless like them in matters such as the disciplinary proceedings or other issues where they could exercise power. It was important to help the managers distinguish between what they were truly helpless about and what they could influence in the changed service.

11

MEETINGS WITH ELDERLY PATIENTS AND CARE STAFF

Introduction

An observational study of hospital and nursing homes for the elderly by Clark and Bowling (1989), confirming previous research, found a lack of contact between elderly patients, only occasional 'comments' passed between staff and patients and rather a lot of negative 'bickering' interactions on wards. A high proportion of patients were described as detached, 'showing no bias or emotional involvement, disinterested, disconnected'. The study concluded that despite the various 'flexible' philosophies of hospitals or homes, 'caring practices are characterised by routinisation and control'. In the work I shall describe in this chapter my hope was to address some of the factors which contribute to this deadly institutionalisation.

Evolution of the patient and staff meetings

> Note how monitoring my own feelings about the work helped me to understand some of difficulties for the staff and patients in being more engaged with each other. See that this understanding helped shape the development of the patient and staff meetings.

When I took up my appointment at the hospital, I began working with an existing staff support group for one of the wards, joining the manager of the hospital in conducting it. I soon started similar support groups for the staff of the other traditional wards, meeting with each fortnightly. (The work of the support groups is described in detail in Chapter 9.) During the first six months the staff brought to the support groups many worries about the changes in the hospital and the uncertainty about their future. They expressed mixed reactions about the groups, including bewilderment, enthusiasm and resentment. I felt increasingly dissatisfied. The shift sytem of work meant there was little continuity of attendance from one meeting to another. Although at times the staff spoke convincingly and with apparent insight about the problems they raised, there seemed little sense of real change as the meetings proceeded. Management, too, were unhappy about lack of development in the staff.

I became aware that by mostly working with staff and some individual patients I had managed to avoid any contact with most of the patients on the long-stay wards. It dawned on me how reluctant I was to engage with these elderly people. I then wondered about the staff's difficulties in being emotionally involved with the patients. It seemed that the primary task for the staff was one of 'servicing' the patients in rigid regimes of getting them out of bed in the mornings, feeding, 'toiletting' and taking them to the day-room or the activity ward and back to bed in the early evening.

I felt the best way of tackling this institutionalisation might be to get more involved myself with the patients, roll up my sleeves and join in. So I proposed discontinuing three of the five staff support groups and replacing them with 'counselling' groups on the three wards for selected patients, which would also include staff. To prepare for this I used the existing structure of the support groups systematically to discuss each patient suggested for such a group to build up a profile about them. I offered the groups to only three wards so that it would be possible to hold weekly meetings. I chose the wards whose staff showed most interest in the work.

The proposal for counselling groups was readily agreed. The detailed preparatory discussions about the patients were popular with the staff and produced some interesting results. For example, we discussed a patient who, prior to hospitalisation, had been described as isolated and in a rather petrified state, reminding me of Miss Havisham from Dickens *Great Expectations*. She was reported to be similarly withdrawn on the ward. At the next meeting I was told she had started a conversation with another patient, the first time this had been noticed. On another ward in which one patient was described as tormenting a new young auxiliary, I talked about how this patient, who had a long history of institutional life, might feel envious of the young auxiliary. I said the auxiliary's distress about being tormented could reflect how the patient felt about her life on the ward. The following fortnight I heard there had been some softening in the relationship, and they had shared a laugh together. Interestingly, the staff rarely acknowledged any connection between these changes and the discussions with me.

The discussions were taking some time, however, usually only creating one profile each fortnight. I could see I had perhaps found another way of putting off direct contact with the patients. I noticed, too, that some of the encouraging results were shortlived: patients and staff soon reverted to old ways of behaving and old complaints. 'Miss Havisham' remained isolated. The young auxiliary and her patient were once again in a persecutory struggle. However, some of the staff were obviously eager to begin the counselling groups and were urging me to make a start. So I quickly concluded the profile-building discussions and talked to each of the patients individually to explain the purpose of the groups: an opportunity to discuss some of their life experiences, aspects of living here on the ward, thoughts and feelings about approaching the end of their lives, even their dreams.

Two of the wards put forward ten patients each. The other only had eight patients left on the ward because, following plans to close it, no new patients were being allocated there. Of the 28 patients only five expressed reservations about joining the groups. I assured them they did not have to attend, but if they changed their minds they would be welcome. Even those who agreed to attend could later choose not to. Some of those I spoke to hardly seemed to take in what I said about the groups, but did not object. A few were keen, saying it was a good idea and giving me the impression that they felt they would be able to help other patients by stories of their interesting lives.

The experience I shall remember from these interviews was of approaching an elderly woman curled up on her bed, her eyes closed and chin resting on her chest. One of the auxiliaries said to me: 'You won't get much out of her!' The staff sat her up, propping her against the pillows. After I had explained the purpose of the group, she opened her wizened eyes and looked straight at me, saying somewhat apologetically: 'I've had a very chequered life.' I replied, 'Well that will be interesting to hear about.' The staff were astonished and commented to me about it. I told her how pleased the staff were that she had been so clear headed. She answered, 'Well, it's variable', and smiled.

Over the next four weeks the two groups of selected patients started well. A few patients talked of their lives before they became ill and even brought some dreams which were about their spouses. They spoke of their fears of dying and their grief for spouses who were dead or who were now only visitors in their lives and for whom they felt a burden. By contrast the third group, comprising all the patients on the ward which was closing, was very hard going. The patients were mostly silent and withdrawn. When a patient did speak from this group, the speech was often fragments from past conversations being relived. In one of the meetings, a woman who had impressed me with her lucidity when I spoke to her individually about the groups seemed to hallucinate. At one time she seemed to be cradling a baby in her arms and talking to it, and at another was putting a dog in a kennel, patting and talking to it.

I realised that in the two easier, selected groups I had created an uncomfortable split between those patients selected into the groups and those who were left out. The groups drew it to my attention. In the group which met in the centre of the ward one of the men angrily asked why they were sitting like a 'load of dummies' by the beds and not with the rest of the patients in the day-room. On the same day the other group, which actually met in its day-room, was silent, whilst outside in the ward the other patients, who were left out, were noisy. We sat in silence, overhearing angry shouting. Remembering that all the patients in one way or another were suffering from loss and abandonment I felt it a mistake to perpetuate a split between the haves and the have-nots in relation to the group meetings. So, after the groups had been running for four weeks, with the agreement of the hospital manager and ward sisters, I arranged to invite *all* the patients and staff on the two wards to attend the meetings.

I spoke individually to the previously unselected patients before the meetings began. It was painfully clear why many of these patients had not been suggested earlier. They tended to be much more withdrawn; some were deaf, some had lost their speech and others were incoherent and confused. I found several of them physically repulsive and smelly; some were unable to sit in wheelchairs and instead were half-sitting, half-lying in 'bean bag' cradle chairs.

Commentary

I believe it was important to start working with staff in the support groups because it was a mode with which they were already familiar. It is like the experience of going to another country and using its currency. Working with the support groups allowed me to find a way into a new situation, to gradually build up a relationship with the staff and to think about the 'work culture' of the hospital (see Chapter 6). The relationships I established with the hospital manager and with the ward sisters became crucial in sustaining an innovation like the patient and staff meetings because the meetings provoked some strong resistance in the staff (see below).

The main trigger to developing the patient and staff meetings was a continual monitoring of my counter-transference (see Chapter 1), sifting through these feelings to discover what they could tell me about the work culture. I saw that my reluctance to become emotionally engaged with the long-stay patients was a significant and probably largely unconscious aspect of how most of the staff felt. This hypothesis from my counter-transference elucidated the findings of the observational research which showed so little interaction in these hospitals. Despite my awareness of this counter-transference issue I still became engaged in a lengthy preparation for the counselling groups which continued an avoidance of involvement with the patients: this was an illustration of the strength of the underlying anxieties that the anticipation of the contact provoked. This process helped me understand why staff would so often say that they didn't have time to spend talking to the patients because there was too much work to be done. Of course there were real difficulties because of the work load and staff shortages, but I think there were also anxieties about spending more time with the patients, anxieties which I had to confront in myself.

Much of the staff's work was devoted to the physical care and well-being of their 'heavily dependent' patients. There were a few staff responsible for 'activities' which took place in a special unit away from the wards, where patients could go during the day if they wished. This arrangement perpetuated a split between what Miller and Gwynne (1993) have identified as a 'warehousing' ideology on the wards, which aims to prolong life, and a 'horticultural' ideology which aims to promote independence in the activities which happen elsewhere. Exploring my own difficulties made me think the staff were apprehensive about feeling more in touch with their patients' emotional experiences of living such a reduced life. If they became more involved trying to help their patients utilise to the full their remaining capacities then they would be confronted with the dreadful limits of what was possible for these elderly people.

I later realised that my experience of frustration about the lack of development in the staff support groups and the preparatory discussions was also a communication from the staff about their frustration with patients who don't get better but only deteriorate and die. When the staff did not acknowledge any connection between some of the improvement they reported and the discussions, I think they also passed on to me their feelings that their own work was not appreciated.

Patient and staff meetings on the Warwick Ward

All the wards were named after fortified castles. I am going to describe the small selected group and then the patient and staff meetings from a ward I shall call Warwick. The patients were typical of those in the hospital. About two-thirds were women. At first there were 8–10 patients in the small selected groups and then usually 15–18 patients attended the patient and staff meetings each week. The meetings were held in the day-room. Three patients stopped attending the meetings, two quite openly, the other in collusion with her relatives who timed their weekly visit to coincide with the meetings. Sometimes patients remained on the ward because they were too ill to attend. About four of the five or six staff on duty attended, not always willingly, but under pressure from the ward sister and the hospital manager who were keen to support the meetings. Some staff stayed on the ward to look after those who did not attend.

About half the patients were seated in their wheelchairs, others were in hospital armchairs and just one or two in easy chairs brought from their own homes. They were arranged in a rectangular configuration in one half of the day-room because of two obscuring columns, which prevented us sitting in a circle. The staff would often have some patients seated in front of the columns when I arrived. I think they regarded my insistence on patients sitting so as to be able to see one another as a funny eccentricity. When the staff re-arranged the patients so they could see, the patients showed little reaction as if it did not matter one way or the other. Only two of the patients had electric wheelchairs and could position themselves.

It took some time for the staff to stop questioning and cajoling the patients to speak, especially at the beginning of meetings or when there were silences. In most meetings few of the patients spoke, but I tried to encourage an attitude of waiting for patients to speak and for staff to speak about their own thoughts and feelings. However, often when I arrived, one of the younger patients, Mrs Bradford (a woman with thick swollen legs) would say in a voice like a school mistress's and full of mockery: 'Be quiet, Mr Terry has come to speak to us!'

The early meetings

Note that an interpretation of the patients' anger enabled them to give voice to some of their complaints and grief. Note, too, that the expression of anger led in subsequent meetings to some liveliness and then closeness through the sharing of sad feelings.

The first meetings were with the selected group. I began by reminding the patients of the purpose of the meeting. Two of the patients, Mr Potter and Mrs Brown, talked briefly about their lives in a rather contented way. Both concluded by expressing their gratitude to the staff for looking after them. The staff started urging other patients to speak, which made me feel angry. I said it was probably difficult for the patients to talk about their feelings if they felt they had to be good and grateful to the staff, especially if they were feeling angry and helpless about having to end their lives living here in this way.

One of the men, Mr Wood, seemed to agree with me. He was a large man, dwarfing his wheelchair in which he sat slumped to one side. His spectacles were a bit lopsided and he peered through them with difficulty. There were traces of spilled food on his clothing. But he gave me the impression of following everything very closely. Most of his speech was incomprehensible to me because it was slurred. Sister Shirley, who could understand him, repeated what he said. He spoke at length about his admission to the hospital and his anger about not being told he was to be admitted for a long time. He had thought he was only coming here on a temporary basis.

In the second meeting Mr Potter talked in more detail about his life and his frustration now at being so helpless. He had severe arthritis and Parkinson's Disease. He tried to make some links between himself and others in the group. He mentioned having been a market gardener and knowing Mrs Cooper, who was seated opposite him. A slight woman with curly grey hair, she appeared to be asleep, with her eyes closed and her head buried in her chest. She did not respond to Mr Potter. She remained silent and as if asleep for most of the time in the first five meetings. (Mrs Cooper finally spoke in the sixth meeting when she talked about how much she missed another woman patient, who had died at least a year before.)

At the third meeting I noticed that all the women had been seated together facing the men. One of the more active women, Mrs Butler, who had an electric wheelchair, seemed to be flirting with Mr Roberts who was severely disabled and seemed to have no speech; he was propped up with several pillows in his chair. She kept gesturing towards him and giggling with some of the other women. He responded with a toothless grin. There was little talk except from the staff who were quizzing the patients to try to get them to speak. Several patients appeared asleep and some others stared into space. I was reminded of a dance with young women and men lined up opposite each other, giggling in embarrassment. I spoke about how painful it must be for the patients to be there like this, as if at a dance but no longer able to dance.

After a while, Mr Holdsworth, who had not previously spoken in the meetings, talked about having been a piano player. He was a small thin man, with sunken cheeks and a soft breathless voice. He was supported by pillows and usually appeared asleep or confused or withdrawn. In my preliminary discussions with the staff they had shown me some early photos of him at the piano with his band and on his wedding day, then a dapper, bright-eyed fellow. He spoke briefly with great effort and then held up his hands, revealing long elegant fingers. Mrs Ferguson, a woman with hearing difficulties, often struggling in vain with her hearing aid, looked at Mr Holdsworth's hands and said they were the hands of a pianist. He said he could no longer play the piano and sobbed bitterly.

Commentary

I think these early meetings show how difficult it is for elderly patients to express their negative feelings, especially their anger when they are so frail and dependent on their carers. My interpretation of the anger, which I understood from my countertransference, seemed to free some of the patients of the pressure to be on their best behaviour, pleased and contented. It was also apparent how reluctant some of the patients were to be in contact with one another. Mrs Cooper's subsequent expression of grief for one of the patients illustrates how the patients sometimes withdrew from contact rather than face the pain of more losses. When there was some lively contact between the patients, as in the 'dance' at the third meeting, the contact brought painful reminders of past lives and poignant feelings of sadness: a telling illustration of the pain that is avoided by passivity and withdrawal. Later there were complaints from the staff that this meeting was upsetting. The complaints expressed their discomfort about the sadness brought by some contact between the patients and illustrates why, unwittingly, staff can collude in the lack of interaction on the ward in order to avoid sad feelings.

Before and after the first holiday break

Note that when all the patients were included in the meetings there was an introduction of madness into the meetings which intensified as the holiday neared. But when some understandng was offered about loss associated with a holiday, the patients were able to talk about how much they missed the staff when they were absent.

From the fifth meeting all the patients on the ward were included in the meetings. At the fifth and sixth meetings a new pattern emerged between Mrs Bradford, a new, relatively younger and fitter patient, and Miss Smith, who was one of the oldest (a woman in her nineties). Both had not previously been in the meetings. Miss Smith, a small wrinkled lady, like a wizened version of Punch and Judy, sat regally with legs outstretched on a stool. Sometimes she called for her lost cat who was given away when she came into hospital and sometimes she asked for 'Emily', who was assumed to be her sister. Just as she apparently did on the ward, she talked at length to no one, though seeming to make eye contact with her neighbours, often smiling and gracious. Much of her talk made no sense because it consisted of fragments of past conversations. Other patients and staff were spoken to as if they were people from her past. She didn't wait for replies or, if replies were given, they were ignored or fitted into the reconstructed conversation.

Mrs Bradford joined in Miss Smith's conversations so as to make fun of her and amuse the others, especially the staff who laughed with her. At times she would get angry with Miss Smith's incessant talk and tell her to shut up. Or, as a theatrical aside, she would exclaim how sad it was to see this 'old dear' talking in this way. I thought it a cruel parody of how the patients felt humoured by the staff. I talked about how horrible it must be to feel ridiculed for being old and helpless, as though the patients had always been old and the staff would always be young.

In the seventh meeting, as we approached the first break in the meetings, for the summer holiday, the ward sister (who had previously attended regularly) was absent. The meeting was dominated by Miss Smith, and Mrs Frost who sat alongside her. Miss Smith was again replaying bits of her old conversations. From time to time Mrs Frost, who had not spoken before and who sat with eyes closed as if asleep, would suddenly lurch forward, as though woken from the dead, eyes wide open, shrieking in response to Miss Smith. But her response was incomprehensible because of a mixture of slurred and confused speech. Only in its intonation did it sound like a reply to Miss Smith, who seemed to be enjoying taunting Mrs Frost. This mad duet went on for some time. I felt helpless and tormented and that listening to it would drive me crazy. Eventually I was able to say how tormenting it must feel to the patients to be so abandoned by their families and friends and by staff such as myself who go on holiday.

Just before the eighth meeting, Mr Holdsworth, the pianist, died. After some time had elapsed in the meeting without any mention of his death, I spoke of it and the feelings it might have stirred. There was little reaction from the patients. Instead, Miss Smith held forth again, immersing us in her imaginary conversations. I interpreted this as a retreat from the awful feelings of abandonment associated with the coming holiday. One of the senior nurses, Ella, angrily disagreed. She told me my holiday was not so important to the patients. After all, she was Miss Smith's keyworker and Miss Smith did not miss *her* when she went on holiday because she knew there would be someone else to look after her!

Later, Ella said she did not agree with my remarks about Mr Holdsworth's death. She herself felt it was not so much his death which upset the patients and staff, because most of the patients and staff were not involved with him, but it was more that his death reminded her and others of folk they had lost. I agreed and thanked her.

When the meetings resumed after a five-week summer break, there was a new patient on the ward, Mrs Shorter, who had become blind late in life. She sat in an armchair, quite immobile, her head tilted back staring at the ceiling, but constantly calling out 'Nurse, nurse, will you help me?' It did not seem to matter who replied, staff or patients, she did not know what she wanted and would soon call out again in the same plaintive way. She was befriended by Mrs James, a tiny woman who was hard of hearing and who wore strong spectacles which magnified her eyes. Mrs James had not spoken previously. She was sitting next to Mrs Shorter, whom she kept reassuring, saying (in slightly slurred speech) that she would help her.

Later, Mrs James started staring at Mrs Bradford, who became angry, objecting to being stared at, even though Mrs James explained that she recognised her because she had a relative who had been a postman who knew Mrs Bradford. This was only the second time there had been any explicit connection made between these patients from links with their lives before they came into hospital, despite them all coming from the local area. Mrs Bradford and Mrs James had been on the ward together for at least two months before this acknowledgement, and then it was unwelcome.

At the next meeting two of the patients, Mrs Bradford and Mrs Frost, were unexpectedly brought back from a week's holiday at a seaside resort. Apparently they had both been too much for the holiday staff to handle. Mrs Frost shrieked throughout the meeting, as she had done before, again lurching forward from her chair, eyes wide open as if she had seen a ghost, calling out incomprehensibly. The staff mentioned that her companion, an elderly man who visited her regularly and who had gone with her on the holiday, had stayed on. I talked about how much she must have missed him, and then she did seem to calm a little. Later, Mr Potter spoke of missing the permanent staff when they were away. He said he then had to put up with 'youngsters' who didn't know him and his 'aches and pains' when they handled him. Mr Wood seemed to agree, but his slurred speech was hard to understand. Sister, who sat alongside him, realised he was referring to missing her when she was absent from these meetings. She looked puzzled and I reminded her that she had been away for the last two meetings before the summer holiday. She was deeply touched.

Commentary

When all the patients were included in the meetings it was clear that what had previously been left out was something quite torturing, represented by Miss Smith's and Mrs Frost's mad rambling, fragmented speech. It is difficult, if not impossible, to disentangle the organic effects of the patients' illnesses from the psychological elaborations of them, but it seems important to give some thought to the psychological components. On all the wards there were patients like Miss Smith or Mrs Frost, who appear to be in a world of their own, reliving past conversations and who can too simply be dismissed as suffering from an organic impairment like dementia. Like some of Valerie Sinason's mentally handicapped patients, I think these elderly patients have developed psychotic defences against the trauma of debilitating illnesses. They suffer the added trauma which Winnicott described, in relation to birth, of the 'intolerable nature of experiencing something without any knowledge of when it will end' (quoted by Sinason, 1986, p.150). In essence they face their own death, knowing it is likely but not knowing when it will occur and how long they must endure waiting to die. Pearl King has found that sometimes fears of death can be avoided by a retreat into psychosis, because in her analysis of some elderly patients she discovered: 'Unconsciously they link mental health with being alive and if they can manage not to be part of life they will not die' (1980, p.159).

I find Robert Hinshelwood's concept of 'dramatization' helpful in thinking about the apparently meaningless exchanges between Miss Smith and others in the meetings. Hinshelwood has described 'dramatizations' in groupwork in therapeutic communities as an 'enactment of the anxieties and defences against them' by the members of those communities (1987, p. 75). In the meetings preceding the first holiday break, I felt Miss Smith and Mrs Bradford, on behalf of all the patients, were engaged in a portrayal of the way staff can humour and infantilise these 'old dears' and how the patients can collude with the staff to maintain defences. The staff can project their own helplessness, dependency and sense of worthlessness into their patients, who, as Simon Biggs (1989) points out, are scarcely in a position to challenge such projections. The infantile dependency relationship that staff experienced in their childhoods can be reversed with their elderly patients. Unresolved conflicts with their own ageing parents, or grandparents, can be acted out by staff. The staff often use their defences to maintain a split between the old patients and the young staff, to protect themselves from the terror of recognising that one day they too might be old and incapacitated like their patients. Reciprocally such splits can be used by patients to protect themselves from unbearable envy, particularly of their able-bodied carers who can walk away from them and return to their own homes and families. Mrs Bradford, a woman with thick swollen legs and feet, often unable to wear shoes let alone walk, would taunt the staff by saying, 'How would you like to be in my shoes?', knowing too well the awful spectre she was of what old age might hold in store for the staff.

The tormenting dialogues which seemed to reach a mad crescendo as the holiday got nearer passed on something of the patients' experience of hospital which they felt would drive them crazy: how so many comings and goings provoke unbearable feelings about past, present and future loss. Ella's reaction to my interpretation about the patients' feelings of loss stirred by Mr Holdsworth's death and the coming holiday shows some of the staff's reluctance to recognise their importance to the patients and the importance of the patients to them. Much later, Ella told me that when she was first training she became very attached to a particular elderly patient. When this woman died, Ella was inconsolable. I felt she was telling me she would never let this happen again because of the terrible pain of the loss. At seminars I conducted for staff, I encountered strong resistance when I scheduled seminars on death and bereavement, beginning with a chapter from Doris Lessing's *The Diaries of Jane Sommers* (1985). The diaries describe a young woman's relationship with an elderly woman who is admitted into long-stay care and subsequently dies there. The seminar had to be repeatedly cancelled because of staff difficulties in attending. One carer openly admitted she wouldn't be coming because she couldn't 'handle bereavement'.

Not only must staff repeatedly confront the death of their patients, but in doing so they are also brought up against their unconscious infantile fears of parents dying and awareness of their own mortality. The denial of death never ceases to amaze me, most of all in myself. I arrived at one ward meeting aware of several empty chairs. On my way through the ward I had passed an empty bed of a woman I knew to have been dying. Few people spoke in the meeting, except for Miss Smith who dominated it with her usual meanderings into the past. Not until the meeting was over, as I walked away with one of the staff and asked about the missing patients, did I allow myself to know about their deaths. I think Mrs Bradford cruelly recognised that the patients whose shoes the staff would certainly not like be in are 'bringers of ambivalent news' (Biggs, 1989, p. 47), because they bring news of ageing, physical decline, impairment and death.

Regimes of 'routinisation and control' and the traditional shift system which ensures that staff are constantly changing despite the commitment to a keyworker approach, are examples of 'social systems' as a defence against anxieties staff would otherwise confront if they had more continuous contact with their patients (Menzies Lyth, 1960). In such ways they unconsciously protect themselves from the guilt at not providing the 24-hour a day familial care that these patients long for (Martindale, 1989b), and avoid the pain of an emotional attachment to patients who will certainly die. Staff are also the recipients of unwanted feelings from their patients, particularly their sense of worthlessness. It has been notoriously difficult to recruit trained nursing staff, reflecting the low esteem of this work and the elderly who are seen as 'non-productive or non-potentially' members of society (Biggs, 1989).

Some community singing and approaching another holiday

See how the counter-transference indicates different feelings expressed by singing in two meetings: in the first the singing contributes to the splitting between staff and patients and in the second it brings a painful closeness. See how the approach of a holiday break again stirs persecutory exchanges in the meetings.

Two weeks later, the meeting was again consumed with the blind patient, Mrs Shorter. She called out repeatedly 'Nurse, nurse, will you help me?' Mrs Bradford kept replying in a humouring tone of voice, offering her blatantly false promises. For example, she offered to take Mrs Shorter to visit her sister, to which Mrs Shorter replied in an equally disingenuous way 'Oh, will you? How nice.' It appeared to me again a cruel parody of staff offering empty comfort to these patients, only to ridicule and triumph over them.

Somewhat later Mrs Shorter, who had a pleasant singing voice, was urged to sing them a song. She obliged and others, even Miss Smith, joined in singing songs such as 'Now is the hour, when we must say good-bye', and 'Keep the home fires burning. . .' and 'I've got a lovely bunch of coconuts'. I felt increasingly uncomfortable about this singsong. It seemed like an awful caricature of what old folk are supposed to do. At the same time I felt I couldn't say this because it would be spoiling the fun. After the singsong I noticed one of the men, Mr Russell, a man suffering with Parkinson's Disease, dementia and poor vision, lean over from his chair and start groping Miss Smith's breasts, until he was stopped by one of the staff. Later, one of the patients and staff talked of arranging 'tea and crumpets' in a rather teasing way, because there seemed to be no real intention of having such a tea. Then Sister rather flirtatiously described my appearance to Mrs Shorter. I felt we were having a 'bit of crumpet', and that the staff were like adolescents flaunting their sexuality at old, impotent parents.

Six weeks later I introduced a microphone into the meetings because I was worried about the patients with hearing problems and those whose speech was faint. I hoped a mike might help, but feared it could be inhibiting. To my relief it was greeted with much amusement. Mrs Cooper, who rarely spoke, announced through the mike that she thought we were all 'barmy', and giggled. Mr Potter graciously asked Mrs Shorter if she would sing him a song and there followed some playful banter between them about his request. She consented and somewhat haltingly, with Sister joining in to help her, sang 'Danny Boy'. A little later we noticed that Mrs Shorter was singing the song again, quietly to herself, this time word perfect, and with enormous feeling. With the aid of the mike we were all able to hear a moving rendition. I felt a heart-rending sadness. Sister and other staff and patients were in tears.

Later in this meeting, I noticed Mrs Jones, a stroke patient who suffered from dementia, was masturbating. Sister was telling her to stop. When I wondered aloud about the masturbation, some of the staff looked disapprovingly at me. But then one of the younger staff described his experience of working with young male amputees in a nursing home where they brought in young women to masturbate them. Towards the end of the meeting Mrs Shorter asked if Mr Wood had lived in a certain street near her home. Mr Wood confirmed he had and Mrs Shorter, who was now blind, said she could remember seeing him. I found this a deeply moving session and later heard that staff and patients thought so too.

Lastly, I would like to describe two meetings which occurred after a mid-term break, as we neared the Christmas holiday. Mrs Shorter was again the focus in both meetings, calling out in a repetitive and tormenting way 'Nurse, nurse, can you help me?' In one of these meetings she was seated alongside Miss Smith, who was repeating her imaginary conversations which became enmeshed with Mrs Shorter's plaintive refrain. The result was that Mrs Shorter appeared to believe that Miss Smith's sister 'Emily' would be taking her out for a walk and she offered to introduce her own sister to 'Emily'. Miss Smith seemed to enjoy this confusion, but also grew impatient with Mrs Shorter, at times telling her to 'Shut up!', much to the merriment of staff and patients.

The next meeting continued in the same vein, except that Mrs Shorter was alongside an auxiliary nurse who stuffed marshmallows or thrust a beaker of cold tea in Mrs Shorter's mouth to silence her. Whenever Mrs Shorter was asked what she wanted, she kept saying she was frightened but didn't know what she was frightened about. There was increasing rage with her; Mrs Bradford joined in telling her to 'Shut up', and other patients and staff taunted her. She seemed unaffected, as though she didn't hear or only heard what suited her. When the auxiliary teased her by offering her 'scotch [whisky] and chocolates', she declined the scotch but accepted the chocolates, apparently not bothered when they were not produced. One of the younger staff said he was surprised I did not get angry like they did when she talked this way, day in and day out. After the meeting I felt I had made some harsh interpretations about what I thought was going on and, when they were ignored by staff and patients, I seemed driven to try even harder.

Commentary

I felt a considerable contrast between the feeling of the singing in the two meetings. The first singsong was preceded by a mocking conversation between Mrs Shorter and Mrs Bradford, which again seemed a portrayal of the way patients felt they were humoured by staff. The singsong seemed a further mocking enactment of a stereotype of old age, mocking those who are taken in by it. It reminded me of the way Sinason (1986, p. 132) describes a handicapped child choosing to behave like the 'village idiot' and 'make everyone laugh [rather] than to expose the unbearable discrepancy between normal and not normal'. So too these elderly patients can present themselves as happy clowns, or sweet old dears, who don't mind what's happened to them, happily engaging in a community singsong.

In the other meeting in which I introduced the microphone I think the patients were touched by my concern about the hearing difficulties and attempt to do something about it. Being in contact with some liveliness and reminders of previous happiness again brought a sadness which Mrs Shorter expressed in her beautiful song, which was both a song of love and of the anticipation of death. The quality of the closeness in this meeting was demonstrable in the way, for the first time, a connection made between two of the patients (Mrs Shorter remembering seeing Mr Wood in the past when she could see) was acknowledged and welcomed.

Sexuality was a theme in both sessions. In the first I thought the staff were flaunting their sexuality in front of the patients at the same time as stopping Mr Russell from displaying his sexual interest. It seemed another way of marking a split between the sexually potent staff and the old impotent patients. By contrast some of the staff's comments about masturbation in the second meeting had more of a quality of concern and even identification with the patients. I had mixed views about Mrs Jones masturbating: on the one hand sex and death seem inextricably linked, as in the song, and on the other it was perhaps used to lift us over the sad feelings. It was also a reminder of the horrible lack of privacy these patients endure on the wards.

The last two meetings show a very different, persecutory mood, in contrast to the beauty and sadness of Mrs Shorter's earlier song. In these meetings her plaintive refrain 'Nurse, nurse, will you help me?' was tormenting and succeeded in provoking anger and ridicule. When patients like Mrs Shorter are provocative in this way, I think it is to try to overcome their sense of no longer being in control of their lives and feeling so helpless. It is a process similar to what Sinason describes about one of her patients who tried to 'draw all abuse on to himself as a way of controlling the disturbance . . . to repeat the trauma into an assimilable experience and to omnipotently compensate for his handicap' (p. 150). In addition, these provocations contributed to maintaining a paranoid-schizoid climate in the meeting. I think my feeling that I had made harsh interpretations shows how I felt drawn into the persecuting culture of the meeting. When I reflected on this in my supervision I appreciated that in the abrasive exchanges in the meeting there had been no room for sad feelings, especially the painful feelings which were stirred by the approach of Christmas. Although I had suggested Mrs Shorter was afraid of dying and that this must have been a fear shared by many there, the interpretation was lost in the persecutory dynamic of the meeting. When Mrs Shorter died unexpectedly a few weeks later, I reminded the meeting of her song which had so painfully anticipated her death:

> Oh Danny Boy the pipes, the pipes are calling
> From glen to glen and down the mountain side,
> The summer's gone and all the roses falling
> It's you, it's you must go and I must bide

But come ye back when summer's in the meadow
Or when the valley's hushed and white with snow
And I'll be here in sunshine or in shadow
Oh Danny Boy, oh Danny Boy I love you so.

But when ye come and all the flowers are dying
If I am dead, as dead I well may be
Ye'll come and find the place where I am lying
And kneel and say 'Ave' there for me.
And I shall hear, though soft you tread above me,
And all my grave will warmer, sweeter be
For you will bend and tell me that you love me
And I shall sleep in peace until you come to me.

(Words by Fred E. Weatherley)

Patient and staff reaction to the meetings

Every few months I met the staff separately to discuss their feelings about the meetings. For the first several months staff were negative, describing the meetings as 'dull', 'boring' and 'depressing'. They were clearly annoyed with me for not introducing topics for discussion or questioning the patients. They reported the patients were complaining that the groups were a 'waste of time' and it was 'scandalous' that I should be paid. Some of the senior nursing staff complained I was upsetting their staff.

Six months after starting the meetings, I was surprised by a shift in the staff attitude on the Warwick Ward. The senior nurse, Ella, said how she had changed her mind about the meetings. She felt the patients were talking more. She described how differently she had come to see Mr Wood, a stroke patient with slurred speech. Previously she hadn't thought much of him, but now she could see that there was a lot to him. I also heard that one of the patients, Mrs Ferguson, who suffered from Parkinson's Disease, said to the ward sister: 'My eyes aren't shutting so much, do you think it could be because of the groups?' She had previously attributed her shutting eyelids to the Parkinson's Disease. I felt cheered by this report because the meetings had perhaps offered this woman another way of thinking about herself and made it more bearable to open her eyes to what was around her. However, the week after I heard this she was seated opposite me in the meeting, her eyes firmly shut! Twelve months later the staff were again quite negative, saying the meetings were just me going on about death all the time.

The meetings on the ward with fewer patients finished after only six months because the ward closed. At the other larger meeting, I was invariably kept waiting to start the meetings because the staff said they had to 'toilet' all the patients after lunch. Few staff attended and then only junior or temporary staff or trainee nurses. I had little doubt I was indeed a 'waste of time'. Following a change of leadership, a new Sister, who was less ambivalent about the meetings, took over and, unlike her predecessor, attended whenever she was on duty. After that patients were assembled on time. Twelve months after the meetings started, again to my surprise, the staff on this ward reported that the patients were more lively and interacting more with one another on the ward. I was told the staff discovered an elderly woman had fallen asleep in her wheelchair but with her head resting on the shoulder of an elderly male patient sitting alongside her.

CONCLUSIONS: COUNTER-TRANSFERENCE ISSUES

Some three years after taking up this work, each time I walked down the long central corridor of the hospital to one of the patient and staff meetings, I was still filled with dread. It didn't get any easier. Yet it was drawn to my attention that in writing about this work I had rather taken for granted the experience and learning which helped me establish and sustain the work. I can see this may be a personal issue but I also think that I became identified with an aspect of my elderly patients: because of their physical and mental decline and current social attitudes towards the elderly, their experience and wisdom can be overlooked, though at the same time these personal resources enable elderly patients to endure what would otherwise be unendurable.

I have written at length about the development of the work to illustrate my considerable ambivalence, particularly about getting more involved with the patients on the long-stay wards. It was thinking about my counter-transference which inspired the innovation of the patient and staff meetings and enabled me to continue. It meant recognising, alongside my conscious interest and enthusiasm about the work, the unconscious fear (and even hatred) of these elderly patients.

A central part of my recurring dread was connected with fears of my own death aroused by contact with the patients. Still in mid-life, I was struck by an image from Elliot Jaques' paper on 'Death and the mid-life crisis' (1965, p. 236; see also Chapter 1, 'Psycho-analytical work with the elderly') where he describes the unconscious meaning of death typical of this stage of life and when persecutory anxieties are uppermost. The image closely resembles the state of elderly patients who are immobilised and mute, but still capable of experiencing physical and emotional pain. I think that close contact with these elderly patients is equivalent to being confronted with

the actuality of one's own worst phantasy of death, where unconscious phantasy and reality become indistinguishable. The trauma
involved is similar to that faced by survivors of disasters who are
brought face to face with their own and others' deaths. Psycho-
analtyic work with survivors has found that the long-term effects of
disasters include difficulties in symbolic thinking because 'thought,
imagination and phantasy can no longer be experienced confidently
as distinct from external reality' and this causes problems for
therapeutic work (Garland, 1991, p. 509). Thus, my own and carers'
and patients' difficulties in thinking seem to be connected with
phantasies of death being concretely experienced in the reality of the
patients' physical and mental conditions.

Another source of attack on thinking was envy, conscious and
unconscious, from patients and staff. I could come and go, unlike
the patients and also the staff who spent many hours on the ward.
When the young auxiliary asked how I could bear Mrs Shorter's
plaintive cries without getting so angry, the uncomfortable knowledge in the question was that it was easier for me because I only had
to put up with it for one hour a week. How can carers bear the
contact for hours each day, day after day? I think they can only
begin to bear it when their feelings are being thought about and
understood. Making the contact bearable means challenging the
various institutional defences against more emotional involvement
with the patients and against reflective or imaginative thought in
those in nursing or caring roles (A. Dartington, 1994).

Much of the staff's concern was about the patients' physical
condition. I felt my role was to introduce some thinking about the
patients' and staff's feelings and the impact of the feelings on those
patients' physical and mental condition. What was most difficult
was to hold in mind an awareness of the physical and emotional
states of the patients, and not-knowing how these states influence
each other. I have found it hard to take in the medical details of the
patients' illnesses and to stomach the sight and sound and smell of
their physical states. I am full of admiration for the loving care the
staff provide for their patients. What enables me to continue
challenging the defences against more involvement is the realisation
that these defences rob the staff of the satisfaction of the reparative
wishes that brought them, and myself, to the work.

The physical condition of the patients provoked and the envious
attacks contributed to maintaining, a persecutory atmosphere as an
avoidance of sad feelings, especially about dying. I was aware of
sometimes being drawn into this avoidance by making interpreta-

tions which could feel critical of staff and patients. My supervisor helped me to be aware of the pressure I felt to be active and perform in some way, instead of simply being with the patients and staff. I had to resist the wish to urge these patients back into health and life which, as Dorothy Judd (1989, p. 148) points out, would be to deny what remains of their dying life and to deny their sadness. I think simply being with the patients means facing a depressive view of death, in confronting a loneliness 'felt to be without remedy' (Pasquali, 1993, p.187), and recognising that whatever hopes may be attached to religious beliefs or life extending through the next generations or one's works, 'death is felt as a void' (p. 189).

For some of the patients, my being there meant allowing a process of 'anticipatory mourning' (Eissler, quoted by Judd, 1989, p. 147), in which patients who are dying gradually detach from loved ones as a way of easing separation and in which the transference relationship becomes a 'substitute arena for the relinquished ties' (p. 147). This is very difficult when so much of therapeutic work is about encouraging attachments. Another aspect of my fears which Judd's work illuminates is her understanding that for those involved with the dying, together with the conscious feelings of guilt and failure there are also primitive phantasies of unconscious impulses of hatred towards loved ones from early life, which can lead to feelings of being responsible for their deaths.

It's when I sat quietly with these patients that I began to feel most like them, old and decrepit. Ruth Porter, in a paper on psycho-analytic psychotherapy in a geriatric unit, draws attention to the need to distinguish the patients' feelings about the damage to their external and internal body image, consequent upon their illnesses, from the worries about physical health stirred in the counter-transference (1991, p.484). It can be no coincidence that since starting this work, for some time I was more concerned about my health and felt more ill (though I was not actually ill) than in any previous work. On a couple of occasions, after leaving the wards to go to a meeting with colleagues in the clinical psychology department, I was embarrassed to find myself dishevelled and spilling food. In patient and staff meetings a new patient repeatedly shouted at me: 'Get out!' I felt humiliated, hurt, terribly unwanted and that I'd better keep my head down and my mouth shut (a painful evocation of how many of these patients feel).

Surrounded by so much illness and damage and despair, I think the experience for patients and carers in their internal worlds is that destructive feelings have got the upper hand. By contrast, listening to the blackbird's song with Mrs Taylor (Chapter 3) or the moving rendition of *Danny Boy* (Chapter 11) were moments of poignant beauty and sadness, when it was possible to regain some confidence in good internal objects, appreciate their beauty and sorrowfully anticipate their loss. It makes me think of Donald Meltzer's work in *The Apprehension of Beauty*, where he postulates that the infant's first experience is of being overwhelmed by its mother's beauty – particularly meaning all the love and care she provides – and by the awareness of the possibility of her loss. Meltzer sees life as a quest to sustain an apprehension of beauty that 'contains in its very nature the apprehension of the possibility of its destruction' (1988, p. 6). I think working with the elderly embodies such a quest in trying to help the elderly and their carers sustain an appreciation of the beauty of life whilst suffering the pain of its ending, a quest which is both difficult and enjoyable.

EPILOGUE: WORK IN PROGRESS

It took a year for the formal contract to be agreed between the purchasers and the private company, and even then many aspects were not finalised. Eighteen months after the move had taken place I was working more intensively with the managers of the two nursing homes on the complex issues still surrounding the move. For some months I continued some staff support groups and smaller versions of the patient and staff meetings in the smaller units within the nursing homes. I realised I was still missing the old hospital, and in some respects behaving as though we were still there. I decided to discontinue the staff support groups and the patient and staff meetings. In their place I established 'multi-disciplinary training seminars' for the staff. The seminars were effectively a case discussion about one patient for an hour each week with those staff most closely involved with the patient and other staff, including the managers, joining in. Amidst all the anxiety and confusion following the move I thought it was important to bring the patients back into focus. The seminars proved popular with management and staff, reminding us all why we were there.

The move led to opportunities for me to work individually with the staff who were responsible for co-ordinating activities, with a view to helping them encourage the care staff themselves to take up an activity role in relation to the patients. So, despite the difficulties of the move, it did seem to lead to more integration within the work between management and staff and patients, between trained and untrained staff and between activity and nursing care.

The patients were given some formal access to the management of the new nursing homes. The private company encouraged the setting-up of a patient and staff committee in which the patients could have their view represented to the house manager and staff. In the first nursing home to establish a committee, it was chaired by a former headmistress. The committee met fortnightly. At first the patient representatives were quite subdued in their contributions but gradually, with the encouragement of the home manager who attended, they became more vocal about their complaints. There were murmurings about the food and the daily menu, requests for a cooked breakfast, then more forceful complaints about the lack of activities during the day. Later, one of the male patients asked why the patients were not represented on selection panels for new staff!

The chairwoman tended to treat the committee as if she were still heading a boarding school and she was inclined to insist that, despite the grievances which were being aired, everyone was 'perfectly happy'. After some time, at the conclusion of one of the committee meetings she burst into tears, saying how lonely and bored she felt in the home. She was a formidable chairwoman and when she died there was much anxiety about whether anyone would be able to replace her. We were taken by surprise because there was strong competition for this post from other patients who were eager to take over.

Still later, I find the managers, because of reductions in their budgets, have become more and more preoccupied with money, trying to make savings on basic items like incontinence pads, or even food. I find it worrying, too, that decisions about such matters seem to be taken by those who are more and more removed from the day-to-day care of the patients.

REFERENCES

A. Bain (1982) 'The Baric Experiment: the design of jobs and organisation for the expression and growth of human capacity', *Occasional Papers, No. 4* (London: Tavistock Institute of Human Relations).

A. Bateman and J. Holmes (1995) *Introduction to Psychoanalysis* (London: Routledge).

S. de Beauvoir (1970) *Old Age* (Harmondsworth: Penguin).

E. Bick (1968) 'The experience of the skin in early object relations' in E. Bott-Spillius (ed.), *Melanie Klein To-day*, Volume 1 (London: Routledge), pp. 187–91.

J. Bicknell (1983) 'The psychopathology of handicap', *British Journal of Medical Psychology*, 56, pp. 167–78.

S. Biggs (1989) 'Professional helpers and resistances to work with older people', *Ageing and Society*, 9, pp. 43–60.

W. R. Bion (1962) 'A theory of thinking' in E. Bott-Spillius (ed.), *Melanie Klein To-day*, Volume 1 (London: Routledge), pp. 178–86.

W. Bolton and V. Zagier Roberts (1994) 'Asking for help: staff support and sensitivity groups reviewed', in A. Obholzer and V. Zagier Roberts (eds), *The Unconscious at Work* (London: Routledge, 1988) pp. 156–69.

I. Brenman Pick (1985) 'Working through in the counter-transference', in E. Bott-Spillius (ed.), *Melanie Klein To-day*, Volume 1 (London: Routledge, 1988), pp. 34–47.

J. Breuer (1985) 'Fraulein Anna O' in J. Breuer and S. Freud, *Studies in Hysteria* (Harmondsworth: Penguin).

P. Clark and A. Bowling (1989) 'Observational study of quality of life in NHS nursing homes and a long-stay ward for the elderly', *Ageing and Society*, 9, pp. 123–48.

E. Cleavely (1993) 'Relationships: interaction, defences, and transformations', in S. Ruszczynski (ed.), *Psychotherapy with Couples* (London: Karnac), pp. 56–69.

W. Colman (1993) 'Marriage as a psychological container', in S. Ruszczynski (ed.), *Psychotherapy with Couples* (London: Karnac), pp. 70–98.

A. Dartington (1994) 'Where angels fear to tread', in A. Obholzer and V. Zagier Roberts (eds), *The Unconscious at Work* (London: Routledge), pp. 101–9.

T. Dartington (1993) 'Clinical Commentary XVI', *British Journal of Psychotherapy*, 10, 2, pp. 258–69.

R. Davenhill (1991) 'Working psychotherapeutically with older people', *British Psychological Society Psychotherapy Newsletter*, December pp. 31–6.

M. Eastman (1993) 'Elder abuse, education and training' in Review Symposium, *Ageing and Society* 13, 1, pp. 115–17.

J. Fisher (1993) 'The impenetrable other: ambivalence and the Oedipal conflict in work with couples', in S. Ruszczynski (ed.), *Psychotherapy with Couples* (London: Karnac), pp. 142–66.

S. Freud (1977) 'Fragment of an analysis of hysteria', in *Case Histories,* I (1901), Penguin Freud Library, vol. 8 (Harmondsworth: Penguin).

S. Freud (1974) 'Transference', in *Introductory Lectures on Psycho-Analysis* (1915–17), (Harmondsworth: Penguin).

C. Garland (1991) 'External disasters and the internal world: an approach to psychotherapeutic understanding of survivors', in J. Holmes (ed.), *Textbook of Psychotherapy in Psychiatric Practice* (London: Churchill Livingstone), pp. 507–32.

F. Glendenning (1993) 'Elder abuse, education and training', in Review Symposium, *Ageing and Society* 13, 1, pp. 117–21.

R. Gordon (1978) *Dying and Creating* (London: Society for Analytical Psychology).

W. Halton (1994) 'Some unconscious aspects of organisational life: contributions from psycho-analysis', in A. Obholzer and V. Zagier Roberts (eds), *The Unconscious at Work* (London: Routledge), pp. 11–18.

W. Halton (1995) 'Institutional stress on providers in health and education', *Psychodynamic Counselling,* 1, 2, pp. 187–98.

P. Heimann (1950) 'On counter-transference', *International Journal of Psychoanalysis,* 31, pp. 81–4.

H. P. Hildebrand (1982) 'Psychotherapy with older patients', *British Journal of Medical Psychology,* 55, pp. 19–28.

P. Hildebrand (1995) *Beyond Mid-Life Crisis* (London: Sheldon Press).

R. D. Hinshelwood (1987) *What Happens in Groups* (London: Free Association).

R. D. Hinshelwood (1989) *A Dictionary of Kleinian Thought* (London: Free Association).

E. Jaques (1965) 'Death and the mid-life crisis', in E. Bott-Spillius (ed.), *Melanie Klein To-day,* Volume 2, (London: Routledge, 1988) pp. 226–48.

D. Judd (1989) *Give Sorrow Words* (London: Free Association).

P. King (1980) 'The life cycle as indicated by the nature of the transference in the psychoanalysis of the middle-aged and elderly', *International Journal of Psycho-analysis,* 61, pp. 153–60.

M. Klein (1935) 'A contribution to the psychogenesis of manic-depressive states' in *The Writings of Melanie Klein,* Volume I (London: Hogarth, 1975), pp. 262–89.

M. Klein (1940) 'Mourning and its relation to manic-depressive states', in *The Writings of Melanie Klein,* Volume I (London: Hogarth, 1975), pp. 344–79.

M. Klein (1946) 'Notes on some schizoid mechanisms' in *The Writings of Melanie Klein,* Volume III (London: Hogarth, 1975) pp. 1–24.

M. Klein (1963) 'On the Sense of Loneliness' in *The Writings of Melanie Klein,* Volume III, (London: Hogarth, 1975) pp. 300–13.

W. G. Lawrence (1991) 'Won from the void and formless infinite: experiences of social dreaming', *Free Associations,* 2, 2, pp. 259–94.

D. Lessing (1984) *The Diaries of Jane Sommers* (Harmondsworth: Penguin, 1985).

B. Martindale (1989a), 'Becoming dependent again', *Psycho-analytic Psychotherapy*, 4, pp. 67–75.

B. Martindale (1989b) 'Review of group psychotherapies for the elderly', *International Review of Psycho-Analysis*, 16, pp. 508–10.

S. McKenzie-Smith (1992) 'A psycho-analytical study of the elderly', *Free Associations*, 27, 3, pp. 355-91.

D. Meltzer and M. Harris Williams (1988) *The Apprehension of Beauty* (Strath Tay, Perthshire: Clunies Press).

I. Menzies Lyth (1960) *Social Systems as a Defence Against Anxiety* (London: Tavistock Institute of Human Relations; 1970).

I. Menzies Lyth (1988) 'A psychoanalytic perspective on social institutions', in E. Bott-Spillius (ed.), *Melanie Klein To-day*, Volume 2 (London: Routledge), pp. 284–99.

D. Millar and V. Zagier Roberts (1986) 'Elderly patients in "continuing care": a consultation concerning the quality of life', *Group Analysis*, 19, pp. 45–59.

E. J. Miller and G. V. Gwynne (1973) 'Dependence, independence and counter-dependence in residential institutions for incurables', in E. J. Miller, *From Dependency to Autonomy*, (London: Free Association, 1993), pp. 67–81.

J. Milton (1994) 'Abuser and abused: perverse solutions following childhood abuse', *Psychoanalytic Psychotherapy*, 8, 3, pp. 243–55.

M. Nolan (1993) 'Carer-dependant relationships and the prevention of elder abuse', in P. Declamer and F. Glendenning (eds), *The Mistreatment of Elderly People* (London: Sage), pp. 148–58.

A. Obholzer (1994) 'Managing social anxieties in public sector organisations', in A. Obholzer and V. Zagier Roberts (eds), *The Unconscious at Work* (London: Routledge), pp. 169–78.

A. Obholzer and V. Zagier Roberts (1994) 'The troublesome individual and the troubled institution', in A. Obholzer and V. Zagier Roberts (eds), *The Unconscious at Work* (London: Routledge), pp. 129–39.

G. Pasquali (1993) 'On separateness', *Psycho-analytic Psychotherapy*, 7, pp. 181–91.

R. Porter (1991) 'Psychotherapy with the elderly', in J. Holmes (ed.), *Textbook of Psychotherapy in Psychiatric Practice* (London: Churchill Livingstone), pp. 469–88.

I. Robbins (1994) 'The long term psychological effects of the civilian evacuations in World War Two Britain', *British Psychological Society PSIGE Newsletter*, 48, pp. 29–31.

M. Rustin (1989) 'Observing infants: reflections on methods', in L. Miller *et al.* (eds), *Closely Observed Infants* (London: Duckworth), pp. 52–78.

S. Ruszczynski (1993) 'Thinking about and working with couples', in S. Ruszczynski (ed.), *Psychotherapy with Couples* (London: Karnac), pp. 197–217.

I. Salzberger-Wittenberg (1991) *Psycho-Analytic Insight and Relationships* (London: Routledge; first published 1970).

J. Sandler, C. Dare and A. Holder (1973), *The Patient and The Analyst* London: Karnac Books, 1979).

H. Segal (1973) *Introduction to the Work of Melanie Klein* (London: Hogarth).

J. Shuttleworth (1989) 'Psychoanalytic Theory and Infant Development' in L. Miller *et al.* (eds), *Closely Observed Infants* (London: Duckworth) pp. 22–51.

V. Sinason (1986) 'Secondary mental handicap and its relation to trauma', *Psychoanalytic Psychotherapy*, 2, pp. 131–154.

V. Sinason (1988) 'Smiling, swallowing, sickening and stupefying: the effect of sexual abuse on the child', *Psychoanalytic Psychotherapy*, 3, 2, pp. 97–112.

V. Sinason (1992) *Mental Handicap and the Human Condition* (London: Free Association).

P. Speck (1994) 'Working with dying people: on being good enough', in A. Obholzer and V. Zagier Roberts (eds), *The Unconscious at Work* (London: Routledge), pp. 94–100.

J. Steiner (1989) 'The aim of psychoanalysis', *Psychoanalytic Psychotherapy*, 4, 2, pp. 109–20.

N. Symington (1986) *The Analytic Experience* (London: Free Association).

M. Waddell (1991) 'The value of soul making: psychotherapy and the growth of the mind', *British Journal of Psychotherapy*, 7, 4, pp. 392–405.

R. M. Young (1995) 'The vicissitudes of transference and counter-transference: The work of Harold Searles', *Free Associations*, 5, 2, pp. 171–95.

V. Zagier Roberts (1994) 'Till death do us part: caring and uncaring in work with the elderly', in A. Obholzer and V. Zagier Roberts (eds), *The Unconscious at Work* (London: Routledge), pp. 75–83.

INDEX